INDICATOR PRACTICE

AND

STEAM - ENGINE ECONOMY.

WITH PLAIN DIRECTIONS FOR ATTACHING THE INDICA-
TOR, TAKING DIAGRAMS, COMPUTING THE HORSE-
POWER, DRAWING THE THEORETICAL CURVE, CAL-
CULATING STEAM CONSUMPTION, DETERMINING
ECONOMY, LOCATING DERANGEMENT OF
VALVES, AND MAKING ALL DESIRED DE-
DUCTIONS; ALSO TABLES REQUIRED
IN MAKING THE NECESSARY COM-
PUTATIONS, AND AN OUTLINE
OF CURRENT PRACTICE IN
TESTING STEAM-ENGINES
AND BOILERS.

BY

FRANK F. HEMENWAY,

*Associate Editor "American Machinist," Member American Society
Mechanical Engineers, etc.*

𝔉𝔲𝔩𝔩𝔶 𝔈𝔩𝔩𝔲𝔰𝔱𝔯𝔞𝔱𝔢𝔡.

FIFTH EDITION.

NEW YORK:

JOHN WILEY & SONS.

1891.

PREFACE.

————

DURING the past two years I have written several short articles for the *American Machinist* on the subject of the indicator-diagram. In these there was not much attempt at connection, or intention to cover more than a few points as they came up from time to time. As an outcome of the appearance of these articles I have received many letters of inquiry, especially from engineers in charge of steam engines and boilers of various classes. These letters, very frequently leading to considerable correspondence, have largely guided me in the preparation of this work: it seemed a fair presumption that they indicated what would be acceptable to others similarly situated.

It has been my aim to present the subject comprehensively enough to enable any engineer to apply the indicator to his engine, take the diagram, and make all necessary calculations from it. The endeavor has been to use no terms except such as are generally understood or fully explained, and no mathematical demonstrations are given or are required that involve the use of anything but simple arithmetical calculations.

As one of the most important ends the indicator can serve is to point out how to bring about economy of steam-consumption, its use has been considered in

connection with steam-engine economy: there seems
to be no rational way of dividing these subjects even
if it were desirable.

A separate chapter has been devoted to locomotive-
engines, because while the general matter applies to
these in common with other steam-engines, there are
some features peculiar to locomotive-indicating.

All the engravings, both of diagrams and methods
of obtaining drum-motion, were made expressly for
this work. What was suitable of the matter referred
to as written for the *American Machinist* has been revised and used; the rest, comprising the larger portion
of the whole, is now published for the first time.

Fully believing that in the near future no engineer
will be considered competent unless he has knowledge
of the use of the indicator, I shall be satisfied if my
efforts make the subject plainer to a few; or if in any
degree they assist those who recognize that the indicator-diagram has become so thoroughly incorporated
with the current literature of steam-engineering, that,
aside from the intention or ability to use the indicator,
every one interested in the steam-engine should learn
to read the diagram.

F. F. HEMENWAY.

NEW YORK CITY, Sept. 1, 1885.

CONTENTS.

CHAPTER VII.

CHAPTER VIII.

CHAPTER IX.

CHAPTER X.

CHAPTER XV.

CHAPTER XVI.

CHAPTER XVII.

CHAPTER XVIII.

INDICATOR PRACTICE AND STEAM-ENGINE ECONOMY.

CHAPTER I.

THE STEAM-ENGINE INDICATOR.

CONSTRUCTION AND USE OF THE INDICATOR.

THE steam-engine indicator is an instrument for measuring and recording pressures. It is said to have been invented by Watt, and employed as a means of improving his engines. In its earlier forms the indicator was crude—hardly up to the standard of the engines upon which it was used. As made at present, it is as nearly perfect as it can be expected any analogous piece of mechanism will be. Its records are universally relied upon, and deductions intelligently made from these records are correct within the limits of present knowledge of steam-engineering. With the comparatively rude instruments used only a few years ago work was done that resulted in great improvement of the steam-engine. With the modern indicator, so nearly perfect in its action, improved as it has been found absolutely necessary to improve it for modern high speeds and pressures, the behavior of steam in

1

the cylinder and in getting into and out of it has been determined and studied in a way to add greatly to the general fund of knowledge in the science of steam-engineering.

The most common use that is made of the indicator is for measuring continuously during the stroke of the piston the pressure in the cylinder of a steam-engine, and recording that pressure on a piece of paper, the record being called an indicator-diagram. The pencil or marking-point with which the diagram is traced is connected by suitable mechanism with a small piston adapted to be moved substantially frictionless in a cylinder. The connection is such that the pencil moves in a straight line up and down with the piston, the motion of the pencil being several—usually four or five—times greater than that of the piston. In use on a steam-engine the indicator is so placed that the cylinder below the piston is put in communication with one end of the cylinder of the engine by turning a small cock. The upper end of the cylinder of the indicator (above the piston) is always open to the at-mosphere; when the cock is turned to close the com-munication between the cylinders of the indicator and engine both ends (above and below the piston) of the indicator-cylinder are open to the atmosphere.

NEUTRAL POSITION OF THE PENCIL.

The motion of the piston of the indicator is con-trolled or restricted by a spring of known tension. When both ends of the cylinder are open to the at-mosphere the pencil will be held in its neutral posi-tion. When the cock is turned to make the connection between the cylinders of the indicator and the engine, if the pressure in the latter is greater than the pressure of the atmosphere, the indicator-piston, and with it the pencil, will be forced, against the resistance of the atmosphere and that of the spring, above the neutral position. When the pressure in the cylinder is less than that of the atmosphere the pressure of the latter will force the pencil below its neutral position, the downward motion of the indicator-piston being resisted by whatever pressure is in the engine-cylinder and by the spring.

The paper-drum has a reciprocating motion on its axis, at right angles to the motion of the pencil. If with the indicator properly attached to the cylinder of the engine the paper is placed on the drum, the latter given a motion corresponding to that of the piston of the engine and the pencil held in contact with the paper, a diagram will be traced from which the pressure against one side of the piston of the engine for an entire revolution of the crank, or double stroke of the piston, may be measured.

SOME OF THE ADVANTAGES OF THE USE OF THE INDICATOR.

The piston of a steam-engine is moved by the pressure of steam against one of its sides. Its progress is resisted by a lesser pressure against its other side, by friction, and by the load upon the engine. The pressure operating to move the piston will always be less per square inch of surface than the pressure in the boiler or steam-pipe supplying the steam, to an extent proportionate to the degree of freedom with which the steam is permitted to pass to the cylinder. Lack of freedom in this respect may be in part due to insufficient steam-pipe or steam-port area, to bends or restrictions in the pipes or ports, to badly arranged or deranged valve-gear, and to other causes, and in part to the operation of the governor in maintaining a pressure to correspond with the load and desired speed. It is of the first importance in the economical use of steam in the steam-engine to know the exact pressure in the cylinder throughout the entire stroke of the piston, and what influences the extent of this pressure. Without the use of the indicator this cannot be known.

The resistance which the piston encounters is in part due to natural and unavoidable causes, and in part to construction and arrangement, subject to changes and modifications. In a condensing-engine this resistance will always be greater than the pressure in the condenser, and in a non-condensing engine greater than the pressure of the atmosphere. Frequently the resistance in either case is materially greater than it should be, and sometimes enormously so. The indicator records this resistance, and if unduly great during any part of the stroke, enables the engineer to locate the trouble, and to determine the effect of the remedy he may apply.

The use of the indicator also enables the engineer to know at any time the power the engine is exerting, and by this means to detect causes outside the engine-room through which steam is wasted. Shafts out of line, injudicious change of lubricants, defects in machines and machinery—causes by which the work required of the engine is increased—leave their mark on the diagram. Increased coal-consumption without corresponding increase of work leads to a search for the cause. The regular use of the indicator is the only way in which the steam-engine can be kept at work economically in the use of steam. Engines have been run for years, wasting thousands of dollars in fuel, when the application of the indicator would have led at once to the detection of the cause of their wastefulness.

To the student in steam-engineering the indicator is an invaluable assistant. Careful consideration of diagrams from different engines, under varied conditions, cannot fail to lead to thought and investigation. Especially is the indicator invaluable if the student must pursue his studies without much help from teachers. By its use many stumbling-blocks will be removed, while the calculations he will be impelled to make in connection with it will lead to the acquisition of a good general knowledge of the whole subject.

CARE REQUIRED IN THE USE OF THE INDICATOR.

Using the indicator is for the most part a matter of common-sense. It is a delicate instrument, and requires careful handling. So is a micrometer-caliper or any instrument of precision delicate in the same sense, and the judgment that applies to the use of one is equally applicable to that of the other. It should be fully appreciated that the entire value of the diagram depends upon its truthfulness: if there is any question of its quality in this respect, it is worthless. If it is supposed to be truthful, and is not so, it is worse than worthless, because misleading. In order that the diagram may be reliable the indicator must be kept in perfect condition, and, when attached for use, the con. nection must be such that the pressure in the cylinders of the engine and indicator will *instantly* be equalized. It is equally important that the motion of the paper-drum shall correctly represent that of the piston of the engine.   No one need expect to succeed in the use of the indicator unless he possess himself of the skill to properly attend to these details.   They are such as will readily be understood by the skilled mechanic, and the necessary skill is quite within the reach of any one who is fit to have the care of a steam-engine.   From lack not so much of skill as a complete appreciation of what is required, unsuccessful attempts to profitably use the indicator may be traced.   The requisites are care in handling the instrument and the habit of thinking—just what are required to properly handle an engine, or to do good work of any kind.   With these, any one can learn to use the indicator without any instruction except such as he may get by reading and study.

CHAPTER II.

DEFINITIONS OF TECHNICAL TERMS.

Absolute Pressure of steam is its pressure reckoned from vacuum: the pressure as shown by an ordinary steam-gauge, plus the pressure of the atmosphere.

Boiler Pressure, or gauge-pressure, is the pressure above atmosphere: the pressure as shown by a correct steam-gauge.

Initial Pressure is the pressure in the cylinder of an engine at or near the beginning of the forward stroke of the piston.

Terminal Pressure (t) is the pressure that would be in the cylinder at the end of the stroke of the piston if the exhaust-valve did not open until the stroke was completed. It may be found by extending the expansion-curve to the end of the diagram. The theoretical terminal pressure is found by dividing the pressure at cut-off by the ratio of expansion.

Mean Effective Pressure (M.E.P.) is the average pressure urging the piston forward during its entire stroke in one direction, less the pressure that resists its progress.

Back Pressure is the loss, expressed in pounds per square inch, due to getting the steam out of the cylinder after it has done its work. On the diagram from a non-condensing engine it is indicated by the distance apart of the atmospheric line and the line of counter-pressure; on the diagram from a condensing-engine it is indicated by the distance apart of the line of counter-pressure and a line representing the pressure in the condenser.*

Total Back Pressure in either a condensing or non-condensing-engine is represented on the diagram by the distance between the line of counter-pressure and that of perfect vacuum.

Initial Expansion is the fall of pressure in the cylinder of an engine as the piston advances and before steam is cut off.

Ratio of Expansion is the proportion the total volume of steam in the cylinder—the exhaust not being opened till the end of the stroke—bears to the volume at cut-off.

Wire-drawing is the operation, accidental or intentional, of reducing the pressure of steam between the boiler and cylinder. Wire-drawing generally, but not always, brings about initial expansion.

Clearance is the space between the piston at the end of its stroke and the valve-face. It is usually reckoned in per-cent of the piston-displacement, or in its equivalent in length added to the cylinder.

The Unit of Heat is the quantity of heat which must be added to one pound of water of a temperature just above the freezing-point to increase its temperature one degree Fahrenheit.

---

* Back-pressure in a condensing-engine is usually spoken of as reckoned from vacuum: this is not correct, as the engine must exhaust against an artificial atmosphere in the condenser, which may be more or less, according to circumstances.

The Unit of Work—foot-pound—is one pound lifted to a height of one foot. One unit of heat is equal to 772 units of work.

A Horse-power (H.P.) is 33,000 pounds lifted to a height of one foot in one minute of time, or equivalent motion against resistance.

Indicated Horse-power (I.H.P.) is the horse-power as shown by the indicator. It is the product of the mean net area of the piston, its speed in feet per minute, and the mean effective pressure, divided by 33,000.

Net Horse-power is the indicated horse-power less the friction of the engine.

Saturated Steam, frequently called "dry steam," is steam that contains just sufficient heat to maintain the water in a state of steam. When saturated steam suffers any loss of heat, some of the steam will be condensed.

Superheated Steam is steam which has an excess of heat: this excess may be parted with without condensation.

Compression is the action of the piston in compressing the steam remaining in the cylinder at exhaust-closure into the clearance-space.

Latent Heat of steam is the quantity of heat, expressed in heat units, required to vaporize or evaporate water already heated to the temperature of the steam into which it is to be converted.

Sensible Heat of steam is its temperature as shown by a thermometer.

Piston Displacement is the space, usually reckoned in cubic inches, swept through by the piston in a single stroke. It is found by multiplying the area of the piston in inches by the stroke in inches.

CHAPTER III.

GETTING READY TO TAKE DIAGRAMS.

HOW TO ATTACH THE INDICATOR.

THE use of the indicator has become so common that the cylinders of nearly all engines are drilled and tapped for its attachment by the builder, as few builders are willing to leave their engines in the hands of the user until after the adjustment of valves by its aid. If the cylinder has not been drilled, the first thing in order is to attend to it. The cock furnished with the indicator is threaded for half-inch gas-pipe tap, and unless the conditions are such that considerable length of pipe must be used, the cylinder should be tapped to correspond. If a horizontal engine, the holes may be drilled in the top or side of the cylinder, or in the heads, as is most convenient for attaching the indicator and getting motion to the drum: they should never be located at the bottom, where they will take water instead of steam, nor where the openings will be exposed to direct currents of steam from the ports. If on the top or side, they should be so near the ends of the cylinder that the piston at the extremes of its travel will not cover them. Occasionally it may be necessary to channel the head or counter-bore of the cylinder a little to provide free opening at all times.

Drilling holes so they are covered by the piston at extreme travel sometimes results in puzzling diagrams.

When the holes are on top of the cylinder, the cocks may sometimes be screwed directly into them, but generally it will be necessary to use a short nipple and coupling to reach through the lagging. When in the side, a nipple and elbow or a bent pipe should be used to carry the indicator a little away from the cylinder and set it in an upright position. The indicator may be set horizontally, when setting it so cannot well be avoided ; but it is always better to set it vertically when practicable to do so. If an elbow is used, it is better for being of a radius four or five times greater than that of an ordinary elbow. It is a good plan to have four such elbows made, cast in brass ; they are likely to be of use some time when it is necessary to make more than one turn in a pipe. If such elbows are not at hand, a very good substitute may be provided by bushing three-quarter-inch elbows. In vertical engines it is best to drill the holes in the side of the cylinder.

LONG PIPES AND BENDS SHOULD BE AVOIDED.

In locating the indicator, the endeavor should always be to use the least admissible length of pipe and the fewest bends practicable. Although steam travels with great rapidity, it nevertheless takes *time* to fill long lengths of pipe, and the current is checked in passing elbows and bends. All pipe and fittings should be free from scale and dirt, and no putty or lead used in making the joints. A little tallow on the pipe-threads will do no harm, but none should be used in the fittings. Before putting the indicator in place, the pipe should be blown through with steam to dislodge any foreign matter that may be inside it, which otherwise might find its way into the cylinder of the indicator. The cylinder and piston of the indicator are easily injured by grit or dirt, hence it is essential to see that the pipes are free and clean. For similar reasons it is not advisable to use an indicator on a new engine until it has been under steam long enough to dislodge and get rid of core sand. All reasonable precautions should be taken to prevent anything except clean steam and the oil used finding its way into the indicator-cylinder.

DIAGRAMS SHOULD BE TAKEN FROM BOTH ENDS OF THE CYLINDER.

It is necessary for all purposes to take diagrams from both ends of the cylinder. When two indicators are used one may be attached to each end, and diagrams taken nearly simultaneously. If only one indicator is used, it must be changed from end to end, or the two ends piped together with a three-way cock at the centre of the cylinder, into which the indicator-cock is screwed. Instead of the three-way cock, a tee may be used with a straight-way cock each side of it. When connected in this way, if the cylinder is more than ten inches diameter, or unless the piston speed is quite slow, it is advisable to use three-quarter-inch pipe. With small cylinders the extent of the valve-opening is correspondingly small, and it will be better to use half-inch pipe with easy bends or large elbows than to depend upon filling the large pipe at the very beginning of the stroke. The pipe may be wound with woollen cloth to partially prevent radiation.

If there are doubts about the truthfulness of the diagrams taken when long pipes are used, they may be verified or set at rest by comparison with diagrams taken from one end with the indicator closely connected. It is undoubtedly true that the use of sufficient pipe to connect the two ends of the cylinder will have *some* effect on the diagram, but the effect has been very much overstated and over-estimated. Under ordinary conditions it will be slight. Still, when practicable, it is better to use two indicators, or, generally, to change one from end to end. This last-named plan is open to the objection that in automatic engines the point of cut-off may change while the indicator is being moved, or that in any engine the load may vary materially in the interval. This is important when it is desired to find the exact load upon an engine at a particular instant, as in the instance of a rolling-mill engine when the piece is passing the rolls. For such a purpose two indicators should be used, handled by two persons.

It is convenient when adjusting the valves of an automatic cut-off engine to take diagrams simultaneously from each end, especially when adjusting to secure equalized cut-off. But with many engines it is possible to arrange so as to conveniently note the position of the governor when indicating one end, and then compare a diagram taken from the other end when the governor is in exactly the same position. Where a large number of diagrams are taken at intervals, as in determining the average power developed, no error will arise from changing the indicator from end to end, even though the power be variable. While the use of two or even more indicators is frequently a matter of some convenience, by the exercise of a little judgment one may be made to serve every ordinary purpose.

Springs of different tension to suit different conditions as to steam-pressure, speed, etc., should be kept on hand. The numbers on the springs signify that a vertical movement of the pencil of one inch is accomplished by a pressure per square inch equal to the number of the spring. Thus, if a 40 spring is used, a pressure in the cylinder of 40 pounds per square inch will raise the pencil 1 inch, or a pressure of 1 pound will raise it $\frac{1}{40}$ inch, and so on. For convenience in measuring pressures from the diagram, scales of pounds corresponding to the different springs are provided. But, as will be readily understood, measurements may be made with an ordinary scale of inches.

For speeds commonly found in practice, springs numbered about one half as high as the steam-pressure employed may be used; for 80 pounds boiler-pressure use a 40 spring, and in that proportion for other pressures. In cases of quite high speeds, however, it is often advisable to use proportionately stronger springs, say in extreme cases a 50 or 60, or even an 80 spring, for 80 pounds boiler-pressure. When the initial-pressure is materially less than boiler-pressure, proportionately lighter springs may be used. In respect to the strength of the spring, it is advisable to use one strong enough to insure a reasonably smooth diagram, but light enough to get a fairly large one.

A spring numbered one half as high as the boiler-pressure may be the rule, to be varied as the judgment and experience of the operator shall dictate.

CARE OF SPRINGS.

Care should be taken not to allow the springs to rust. Even if nickel-plated, rust may attack them in spots. To guard against this they should never be left in the indicator when not in use; remove them, wipe carefully, and wrap in a piece of tissue-paper, well oiled.

CLEANING AND OILING THE INDICATOR.

After use, the inside of the cylinder of the indicator should be wiped quite clean and dry with a piece of soft waste on a stick or long pencil. It should never be put away dirty. Before use the cylinder should be well oiled, using oil of the best quality. A little oil should also be applied to the joints.

CHAPTER IV.

DRUM MOTION.

WHERE TO TAKE THE MOTION FROM.

THE motion for the paper-drum is very commonly and conveniently taken from the cross-head, reduced to give the length of diagram desired. In beam-engines it is frequently taken from the beam. No plan for reducing the motion from the cross-head is universally applicable; circumstances must determine what plan can best be employed, and good judgment used in getting a motion that will, on a reduced scale, represent that of the piston. A few examples are given which will suggest others to suit existing conditions. Referring to these, in Fig. 1 the reducing lever *a* is pivoted overhead to a temporarily arranged plank or timber, which may be extended down from the overhead flooring, or it may be a scantling braced from the top of the engine-bed to the ceiling—any arrangement that will present a suitable surface at the proper height. The segment *b* is made fast to the lever so that its semi-circumference is true with the pivot *f* upon which the lever swings, but may be set at any angle with the lever. The radius of *b* must be such as to give the required reduction of motion; that is, the radius should bear the same proportion to the length of the lever as the proposed length of diagram bears to the stroke

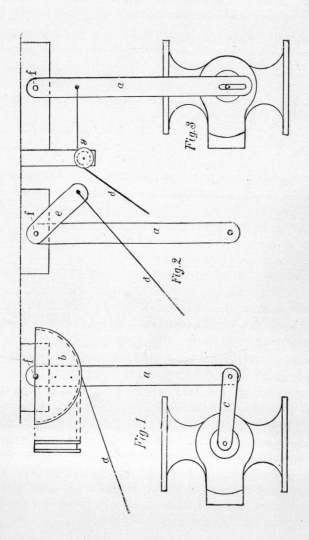

Fig. 3

Fig. 2

Fig. 1

of engine. The radius may be readily found by multiplying the length of the lever by the proposed length
of diagram, and dividing by the stroke of the piston.
For instance, suppose the length of diagram is to be
4 inches, the stroke of piston being 24 inches, and the
length of lever 40 inches: $40 \times 4 = 160$, which divided
by 24 gives for radius of b $6\frac{8}{12}$ inches.

At the lower end the reducing-lever is connected by
a short connection c to a pin fast in the cross-head, or
in an angle-iron made fast to the cross-head.

The lever a may be of any convenient length, not
less than about one and one half times the stroke of
the engine. The length of connection c may be about
one half the stroke of the engine, more or less. When
the cross-head is at mid-stroke the lever a should stand
in a vertical position, and the connection c should,
during the stroke of the engine, vibrate equally above
and below a horizontal position.

With this arrangement the cord d may be led to the
indicator in any direction in line with the swing of the
lever a, the piece b being moved, if necessary, to ac-
commodate the direction; it is evident that the motion would not be changed except in direction, which
is immaterial, if b were turned one half around from
the position in which it is shown, bringing the arc at
the top. Two cords may be led from b to as many
indicators, if desired.

An objection to this reducing motion is that the
piece b must be turned true, and then will not suit
different conditions as to stroke, etc. But if the lever
a always bears the same proportion in length to the
stroke of the engine on which it is used, which in the

majority of instances it may be made to do, then the
same piece *b* will give diagrams of the same length, no
matter what the stroke of the engine is. By leaving
half the hole (the size of pivot or screw at *f*) in *b* it
can be readily attached to any lever, so as to fulfil the
conditions of being true with the pivot ; or since the
whole of a circle will naturally be turned in making *b*,
the whole of the hole may be left in it, forming the
bearing for the pivot.

Another form of reducing-lever is shown in Fig. 2.
This is pivoted and connected to the cross-head, the
same as that shown in Fig. 1 ; but the cord is attached
to a piece *e*, so that a line drawn from pivot *f* to the
point of attachment shall be at right angles to the
cord leading to the indicator when the lever *a* is vertical and the engine at mid-stroke. The direction of
the cord to the indicator may be at any angle up or
down, but must be in line with the swing of the lever.

In Fig. 3 the lever *a* is slotted at the lower end, and
works on a pin in the cross-head. The cord is attached
directly to the lever or to a projecting screw, and must
leave the lever at right angles to it when in a vertical
position, and in line with its swing ; hence with this
reducing motion it is generally necessary to use a small
guide-pulley represented at *g*. After leaving the guide-
pulley the cord may lead in any direction whatever to
the indicator. The distance from pivot *f* to the point
at which the cord is attached will be the same in the
last two examples of levers as the radius of *b* in the
first example, and may be found in the same way.

All the parts of these reducing motions are represented as made of wood. If a permanent arrangement

is desired they may be made of metal. In any case the joints should be free from lost motion.

A variety of modifications may be made to suit different conditions. The lever may extend downward instead of upward, or horizontally to either side. More than one guide-pulley may be used: it is better, however, to use as short and direct cord as possible, and if practicable to avoid the use of guide-pulleys altogether; this is especially advisable at high speed.

Generally,—particularly on short-stroke engines,— when the reducing motion is to be used regularly on one engine, or on engines of the same class, a standard for the upper pivot of the lever may be attached to some part of the bed so as to be put up and taken down quickly.

Planning for attaching the indicator and getting the drum-motion should be simultaneously done. Sometimes the indicator, by the exercise of a little forethought, may be arranged to greatly simplify the connecting to the drum; sometimes a particular arrangement of the drum-motion will permit the indicator to be much more advantageously set. Generally the whole matter is simple, but in special instances, where there is but little space to work in, considerable ingenuity will be required. Attention must be paid to the arrangement of levers and to the direction in which the cord is led, as has already been referred to. Reflection will show that if this is not done the motion will not be correct. When the temptation is to lead the cord a little indirectly from the lever, the effect of doing so may be better seen by, in imagination, going to the extreme in the same direction. And the same is true of setting the lever so that it does not vibrate equally to each side, etc. A correct understanding of what is wanted must first be had, then judgment used in obtaining it. The reduced motion by levers will hardly ever be *absolutely* correct, but when properly arranged the variation will be unimportant.

Other means than simple levers are sometimes employed for giving motion to the paper-drum. Sometimes a pantograph, so called, is used; sometimes reducing-wheels. The writer has never found anything so satisfactory as one of the three arrangements shown in Figs. 1, 2, and 3, preferably used without the guide-pulley; hence others will not be described.

It is perhaps needless to say that the reason why the use of a short direct cord is to be preferred is that the shorter the cord the less it will stretch, and guide-pulleys may cause slight irregularities, besides stretching the cord more because of increased friction and inertia.

LENGTH OF DIAGRAMS.

It is advisable to take a fairly long diagram, because if all the motions are correct the longer the diagram the less the liability to error in measuring it. A long diagram is also better than a short one when taken for adjusting valves, because slight variations are represented at correspondingly greater magnitude. On the other hand, and particularly at high speed, the attempt to get large diagrams will sometimes introduce errors of greater importance than those it is sought to avoid. On long-stroke engines diagrams may be taken as long as five inches, but four and one half inches is better practice. From this length as the extreme they may be taken four inches, three inches, two inches, or even less—according to speed and other conditions. Judgment must be used in this respect. At high speed the inertia of the paper-drum becomes an important factor, and if the attempt is made to take a full-length diagram this will in some degree affect its truthfulness.

BEST CORD TO USE.

The best cord to use is of braided linen, about one twelfth inch in diameter. It should be well stretched before being used, by attaching one end to something overhead and hanging a weight on the other end, allowing it to remain in this condition not less than twenty-four hours (it should not be allowed to untwist in being stretched); then go over it with a piece of bees-wax and afterward with a piece of wood with a notch in it, keeping it well stretched at the time. When thus treated, it may be wrapped in paper and laid in the box for future use. It will be found not liable to stretch, and will not be readily affected by water or steam. So much wax should not be used as to make the cord stiff and unwieldy.

If a steel hook or ring is used for connecting with the hook on the indicator it should be quite light, or it may cause the cord to "throw."

CHAPTER V.

TAKING THE DIAGRAMS.

ADJUSTING THE LENGTH OF THE CORD.

THE indicator may be swung around one way or the other, and the piece carrying the guide-pulleys at the lower end of the drum may be moved so as to lead the cord fairly. After fastening the hook, or making a loop, so that the cord is presumably the right length, take hold of the end of one cord with each hand, letting one follow the motion of the reducing-lever, keeping the cord taut, and with the other pull the drum around from one stop to the other, observing if the cord needs lengthening or shortening to insure the drum travelling about as near to one as to the other. Having lengthened or shortened the cord, if necessary, hook the two cords together and note if the motion is smooth.

ADJUSTING THE PAPER AND PENCIL.

The paper should be so placed on the drum that the clips hold it stretched quite smoothly and evenly, otherwise the diagram will be distorted and worthless. Sharpen the pencil to a smooth fine point; a piece of fine sand-paper is best for this purpose. Adjust the pencil-stop so the pencil will bear no harder than just sufficient to make a plain mark: harder than this creates unnecessary friction and makes the diagram untrue.

Everything being in readiness, the pencil out of contact with the paper, open the indicator-cock and hook the cords together. At high speeds some little difficulty will be experienced in connecting the cords, but a little practice will overcome it. By this time the indicator-piston will have made a few strokes, and the indicator-cylinder will be warm; then move the pencil up to the paper and hold it there while the engine makes a double stroke and the pencil traces the diagram. Swing the pencil away, close the cock, and *immediately* return the pencil and trace the atmospheric line; then unhook the cords.

This being the first diagram, it is important to know that the indicator is working properly. One precaution that may be taken to that end is to again open the cock, let the piston make a few strokes, then close it, and, bringing the pencil close to the paper, turn the drum by hand and observe if the pencil covers the atmospheric line just traced; then note if a slight pressure up or down on the pencil-lever will cause the pencil to stand above or below the atmospheric line. The pencil at these tests should cover the atmospheric line: if it fails to do so, the pencil movement is not free in the joints, there is lost motion, or the piston is not free in the cylinder. The piston should be kept well oiled, and the freedom of the pencil movement should be tested before putting in the spring.

Being sure that the indicator is working quite freely, as many diagrams as are desired may be taken, as fast as each one is removed from the drum such memoranda as seem pertinent being made upon it.

PRINTED BLANKS.

Printed blanks may be had from the printer at a trifling expense. They are convenient, always ready for use, and make it probable that data that will perhaps some time be valuable will be preserved. They should be, for an ordinary drum, about $3\frac{1}{4} \times 7\frac{1}{8}$ inches. Those used by the writer are printed as follows:

Diagram taken by_____at _____ 188___

From_____End of_____Engine.

Built by_____

Diameter___Stroke___Clearance___Revolutions___Boiler-pressure___

Vac. per gauge_____Air-pump diameter_____Stroke_____

Tem. of Injection_____Discharge_____

Diameter of steam-pipe_____Length_____

Diameter of exhaust-pipe_____Length_____

Tem. of feed_____Valve gear_____

Governor_____Position of throttle_____Vertical scale_____

Remarks.

CHAPTER VI.

READING THE DIAGRAM.

ABSOLUTE INFORMATION CONVEYED BY THE FIGURE TRACED.

HAVING taken the diagram, the next consideration is how to read it. The figures traced by the pencil will vary widely under the different conditions of different engines from which the diagrams are taken, or from the same engine under different conditions; and it is necessary to know how to interpret these variations—to reason back to the cause that produces the effect. The only absolute information the diagram conveys, whatever its form, is the pressure in the cylinder of the engine. All the other information to be had from it comes through processes of reasoning.

Knowing that the pencil will at all times stand at a height corresponding to the pressure in the cylinder, ánd that the length of the diagram will, on some scale, represent the stroke of the engine, it will be readily understood that if steam of full boiler-pressure was admitted to the cylinder at the beginning of the stroke, and maintained to the end; if then all the steam was instantly discharged and the piston returned against the pressure of the atmosphere if the engine is non-condensing, or against no pressure if condensing—the figure described by the indicator-pencil would be a rectangle, the height of which would represent the pres-

sure of steam in the boiler, and the length the stroke
of the piston. If it were possible it is not desirable

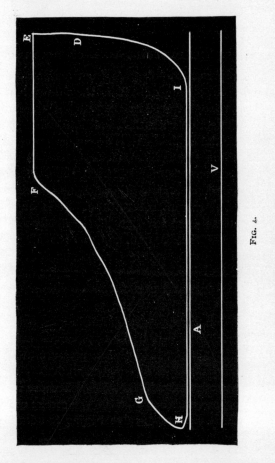

FIG. 4.

that the construction of the engine should be such as
to produce this diagram. Yet such a diagram would

represent some good features—better than are obtained in practice. But it would show a lack in one essential feature; that of taking advantage of the expansive property of steam.

NAMES OF THE DIFFERENT LINES OF THE DIAGRAM.

Fig. 4 represents a diagram from a non-condensing automatic cut-off engine. *A* is the atmospheric line. This line, though traced by the pencil of the indicator, has no connection with the conditions existing in the cylinder of the engine. It is drawn, as previously explained, when the indicator-cock is turned so as to close the communication between the indicator and engine cylinders, and with atmospheric pressure on both sides of the indicator-piston. It is of the first importance to establish this line correctly; it is the neutral line of the diagram, and from it all pressures above and below it must be determined.

V is the line of perfect vacuum, or no pressure : this line is drawn by hand at a distance below *A* equal, by the scale of the spring, to the pressure of the atmosphere. When this pressure is not known, it is at ordinary altitudes assumed to be 14.7 pounds per square inch. This is about the average pressure at the sea-level ; at high altitudes it is materially less.

DE is the admission-line, so called because its beginning, *D*, represents the point in the stroke of the engine at which the steam-valve begins to admit steam to the cylinder.*

---

* The terms "steam-valves" and "exhaust-valves" are, for convenience, used without reference to whether the engine has one or four valves.

EF is the steam-line, considered as beginning at the point of positive change in direction of the admission-line, as at *E*, and terminating at the point of cut-off, *F*.

The expansion-line, *FG*, is traced after admission of steam to the cylinder has ceased, the pressure falling by expansion while the piston is travelling a distance represented on the diagram by the distance horizontally from *F* to *G*.

The exhaust-line begins with the opening of the exhaust-valve at *G*, and continues to the end of the forward and beginning of the return stroke.

HI is the line of counter-pressure, beginning with the return stroke and continuing to *I*, at which point the exhaust-valve is closed.

The compression-line begins at *I* and continues to *D*, the pressure rising as the steam remaining in the cylinder is compressed into less volume, substantially as it fell with the increase of volume during expansion.

This designation of lines is to a certain extent conventional, and is adopted more for convenience than for exactness of expression. The admission-line, for instance, might properly enough be considered as continuing from the time of opening till that of closing of the steam-valve, and the exhaust-line from the opening till the closing of the exhaust-valve ; but they are more conveniently referred to when further divided, as noted.

The beginning and termination of some of these lines are called points, and their continuation periods in the stroke of the piston. Thus *F* represents the *point* of cut-off and *FG* the *period* of expansion.

DATA NECESSARY AND USEFUL.

The names of the lines of the diagram are the alphabet, as it were, by which it is read. As a further aid in comprehending it several things having reference to permanent and accidental conditions should be known. Those more particularly essential are noted on page 25. Diagrams are often practically worthless because so little is known about the conditions under which they were taken : hence the data should be made as complete as practicable. When this is done their study is pleasant and profitable, showing, by comparison, the effect of different construction and operation.

THE USE OF THE INDICATOR FOR ADJUSTING VALVES.

One of the uses of the indicator, and an important one, is in adjusting the valves of all classes of steam-engines. However carefully valves may be adjusted when the engine is not under steam, expansion, and perhaps some springing of parts, will cause derangement—sometimes serious—when the engine is working. In many engines having automatic valve-gear derangement by wear of some of the parts is likely to bring about improper and expensive action ; in fact in any engine derangement will always occur by the wearing of parts. In all such cases the indicator is a ready means of locating the trouble. Builders do not consider their engines completed until the final adjustment of valves by the use of the indicator ; users cannot be assured that their engines are working economically except by the regular use of this instrument.

LEAD.

Suppose the indicator is applied to an engine, the result being a pair of diagrams similar to those represented in Fig. 5. In Fig. 4 the admission-line is vertical, showing that the steam-valve opened sufficiently to admit steam to fill the clearance-space at about boiler-pressure before the piston began its stroke. In *A*, Fig. 5, the admission-line is inclined in the direction

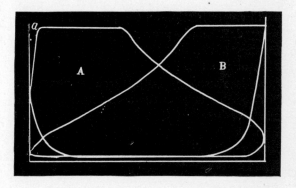

FIG. 5.

of the stroke of the piston. We should infer that the valve began to admit steam just as the piston began its forward stroke, instead of, as is the more common practice, just before the termination of the return stroke. Just how far the piston has moved before full pressure is admitted may be readily determined. Measuring the distance at *a* it is $\frac{1}{8}$ inch, and the length of the diagram is $2\frac{5}{8}$ inches; $\frac{1}{8}$ inch is $\frac{1}{21}$ part of $2\frac{5}{8}$ inches, so the piston has made $\frac{1}{21}$ part of its stroke up to the point of full admission. If the stroke is, say,

12 inches, the piston has moved $\frac{12}{21}$ inch up to this point.

Generally prompt admission, as in Fig. 4, is favored by engineers, the argument being that the cylinder and piston having been cooled during exhaust the exposed surfaces should be heated as early in the stroke as practicable. On the other hand, it is reasoned by those who favor late admission, that, while the crank is at and near the dead-centre pressure against the piston will have no effect to turn the shaft, but on the contrary will create friction on the pins and main journals, which tends towards preventing its turning; for this reason they advise that the pressure in the cylinder be kept low at this time.

There is reason in both these arguments. The writer does not believe there is much of either loss or gain in admission that is a trifle late,* and would always make it such as seems to bring about the best conditions otherwise. When the ports are small or when the clearance is large late admission may result in a low steam-line (low compared with boiler-pressure), which is a condition unfavorable to economy; in such cases the valve should have lead. In other cases it may or may not have lead, according as the engine runs smoother with or without it.

Referring to *B*, Fig. 5, from the other end of the

---

* These terms are used in accordance with the custom of speaking of lead as the extent of the opening of the steam valve, in the line of its travel, with the crank is on its dead-centre; early admission, such as results in an admission-line as in Fig. 4 ; lack of lead, no opening of steam-valve until the piston has commenced its forward stroke; and late admission, as in *A*, Fig. 5, the result of lack of lead.

cylinder, it will be seen that conditions contrary to those in *A* exist; that the steam-valve on this end opens considerably before the end of the return stroke. (By forward stroke, that stroke of the piston in which steam is admitted to the end of the cylinder under consideration is understood; by return stroke, its stroke in the opposite direction.) The lead is excessive on this end. Equalizing the lead will make it about like that in Fig. 4 on both ends. If both diagrams were like *A*, the eccentric should be advanced to bring this about; if like *B*, it should be moved back to reduce the lead.

EARLY AND LATE EXHAUST-CLOSURE.

A, Fig. 6, shows too much compression. By early exhaust-closure the pressure behind the piston is in

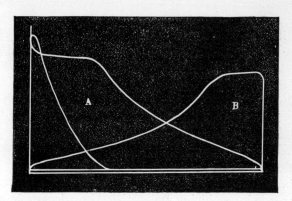

Fig. 6.

creased, until before the completion of the return stroke it is higher than that in the steam-chest; then when the steam-valve opens the pressure falls, making a loop in the diagram. The remedy for this is to bring about later closure of the exhaust-valve. Modern practice largely favors, when practicable, an exhaust-closure that will compress the imprisoned steam to about two thirds as high as initial pressure. Fig. 4 shows compression to that extent, and is about right.

The argument in favor of compression is, that it fills the clearance-space with steam that would otherwise be wasted, and thus effects a direct saving of steam, which is true to a certain extent; also, that it tends to smooth running, which is equally true. There is always some looseness in the main journals and connecting-rod boxes, and this if taken up suddenly, as it is when steam of high pressure is instantly brought to act on the piston, produces a jar or pound. If the exhaust-valve is closed at the proper time in the stroke, the pressure on the exhaust side of the piston increases till it equals and then becomes greater than the pressure urging the piston along: this comes about so gradually that the tendency is to take up what lost motion there may be in the same gradual manner.

Increasing compression will not always stop pounding in an engine; but when it is quite low, increasing it will generally have an effect that way. Some engines run satisfactorily, so far as jar is concerned, with little or no compression. To be of much service in bringing about smooth running, compression should be carried to a higher point than the pressure in the other end of the cylinder at the termination of the stroke. If we suppose the diagram from the other end of the cylinder to be a duplicate of that shown in Fig.

4, then the pressure at the end of the compression-line, as at *D*, should be higher than at *G*. If the pressure is enough higher at *D* than at the end of expansion to have gradually overcome the forward pressure, and the momentum of the reciprocating parts, all will have been done that can be by compression to insure still running. To insure an arresting of tendency to motion in one direction and a tendency to motion in the opposite direction of the reciprocating parts, the pressure, except in the case of low speed, must be materially higher at *D* than at *G*.

In *B*, Fig. 6, the exhaust-valve closes too late. There is no compression, showing that the exhaust is open until the end of the stroke. The exhaust-valve should be made to close earlier in *B* and later in *A*.

EARLY EXHAUST-OPENING—BACK-PRESSURE.

Moderately early exhaust-opening, as represented at *G*, Fig. 4, gives time for the escape of steam before the piston begins its return stroke, and assists in keeping the back-pressure low. As the piston gets near the end of its stroke, pressure on it is nearly all, then entirely, spent in creating friction : so it is always advantageous in this respect to open the exhaust before the end of the stroke. It is very seldom that diagrams from stationary engines are seen which represent actual loss from too early exhaust-opening : very frequently diagrams that represent a loss of from one to five pounds in back-pressure from late exhaust are met with. The matter of exhaust opening and closure is only to a limited extent in the hands of the engineer, as it is largely controlled by the designs of the builder.

The engineer frequently finds himself obliged to com-
promise as between too much tendency to pound and
a loss from back-pressure.

The back-pressure in a non-condensing engine, represented by the distance apart of the atmospheric line
and the line of counter-pressure, varies with the construction of the engine, the speed at which it runs, and
the adjustment of the valves, and to a considerable
extent with the pressure in the cylinder at exhaust-
opening. Sometimes it is as little as one-half pound
—even less; but two pounds is nearer an average.
Excessive back-pressure may be caused by small ports,
small exhaust-pipe, or tortuous passages. Late exhaust-opening, as previously referred to, tends to increase back-pressure; the presence of water in the
cylinder has the same tendency.

WAVY LINES—SERRATED LINES.

The wavy lines of Fig. 7 result from natural causes—
from high piston-speed, reaction of the spring, and
momentum of the reciprocating parts of the indicator.
When the waves are symmetrically rounded and not
too intense—not much more so than in Fig. 7—they do
not materially affect the truth of the diagram. When
the undulations are considerably more intense than in
this figure, the remedy is to use a stronger spring, and
sometimes to shorten the motion of the paper-drum.

Serrated lines, as in Fig. 8, are evidence of undue
friction in some of the parts of the indicator, and make
the diagram worthless. Sometimes when the instrument is new the piston may be a trifle tight—so much

so as to stick in the cylinder. The remedy is to attach the indicator to an engine (not connecting the drum-motion), and, keeping all parts well oiled, let it work

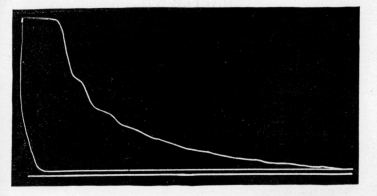

Fig. 7.

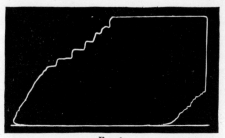

Fig. 8.

for an hour or two. If the instrument is not new, it requires cleaning and oiling, and an examination to see that there is no derangement of parts.

CHAPTER VII.

HEAT—THE EXPANSION OF STEAM.

HEAT.

WE speak of the consumption of steam by the steam-engine, but behind this is the well-known fact that a certain amount of steam represents a definite amount of heat. Heat is converted into work,—motion against resistance, — steam being the medium. This heat appears in tangible form in the furnace : a portion of it is transferred to the water in the boiler, some of it escapes through the chimney, and some of it warms the surrounding air. Of the heat that is utilized in making steam, some is lost before it reaches the cylinder, some by radiation from the cylinder, and some is transformed into the work of moving the piston against the resistance it encounters. But the greater part of it finds its way out of the cylinder with the exhaust-steam, into the condenser or the atmosphere. It is not possible, in the light of present knowledge, to realize as motion in the machinery more than a small percentage of the heat that appears in the furnace ; economy in steam-engineering consists in part in making this percentage as large as practicable.

HEAT OF COMBUSTION OF COAL.

The heat of combustion of one pound of coal of good quality is 14,500 heat-units, each equivalent to

772 units of work. If then the heat of combustion of one pound of coal could be employed in raising a weight of one pound, it will raise it a distance of $14,500 \times 772 = 11,194,000$ feet, or more than 2000 miles! We may very readily see what proportion of this work is done in the steam-engine by the heat from one pound of coal burned in the furnace. Suppose this pound weight to be raised to the height named in one hour. A horse-power is 33,000 pounds raised one foot high in one minute = one pound raised 33,000 feet in the same time, or 1,980,000 feet in one hour. Then $11,194,000 \div 1,980,000 = 5.65$ horse-power exerted for one hour will raise this weight. It is an exceptionally good steam-engine that will develop a horse-power per hour with the consumption of 1.75 pounds of coal; and with such an engine to do work equal to raising this one pound weight 11,194,000 feet would require $5.65 \times 1.75 = 9.88$ pounds of coal, about 10 per cent of the heat of combustion being made to do useful work in the cylinder.

BOILER DUTY.

When coal is burned by natural draught in the furnace of a boiler from 18 to 24 pounds of air must be admitted for each pound of coal burned. To maintain the necessary draught, the gases must enter the flue at a temperature of from 400° to 600°, carrying with them considerable heat. The heat passing off through the chimney, lost by radiation from furnace, etc., and by unconsumed fuel, may be taken under favorable conditions to be 30 per cent of the heat of coal: it is seldom less than this, and frequently much more. The heat transferred to the water is then about 70 per cent, or $14,500 \times .70 = 10,150$ heat units per pound of coal.

THE CONVERSION OF WATER INTO STEAM.

Assume one pound of water at a temperature of $40°$ to be converted into steam of the pressure of the atmosphere. To bring this water to a temperature of $212°$, the boiling-point, there must be added $212 - 40 = 172$ units of heat.* If the heat is continued and the steam allowed to pass freely into the atmosphere 965.7 more units of heat must be added, making altogether 1137.7 heat-units imparted to the pound of water. These 965.7 heat-units are the latent heat of steam at atmospheric pressure. The latent heat of steam at other pressure may be found from Table II., as explained in the text immediately following the table.

If steam of 100 pounds pressure is to be generated in a boiler, we find from the table that it will contain 1213.8 heat-units per pound. If the water is heated, as in a feed-water heater, to $160°$, there must be imparted to it $1213.8 - 160 = 1053.8$ heat-units. Then the $10,150$ heat-units mentioned in a preceding paragraph would evaporate $10,150 \div 1053.8 = 9.63$ pounds of water. This result is considerably above the average.

---

* This is not strictly correct, because as the temperature of the water is increased above $40°$ the addition of a unit of heat will raise its temperature slightly less than one degree ; but the decrease is so slight, amounting altogether to less than one degree from $40°$ to $212°$, it need not be considered. For all ordinary purposes we may calculate that if we add one heat-unit to a pound of water below $212°$ it will increase its temperature one degree.

THE EXPANSION OF STEAM—MARIOTTE'S LAW.

Steam expanding in the cylinder of an engine doing work follows with reasonable exactness the law of gases known as Mariotte's law, the pressure varying inversely as the volume. According to this, if steam of 80 pounds absolute pressure per square inch is admitted to the cylinder of a steam-engine for one half the stroke, neglecting clearance for the time being, the pressure at the end of the stroke will be 40 pounds; or if the steam follows one-quarter stroke, the pressure at the end of the stroke will be 20 pounds; etc. In the first-named instance there is a pressure against the piston of 80 pounds, absolute, per square inch for one half the stroke, and for the other half the pressure varies from 80 pounds to 40 pounds. In the second instance the pressure is 80 pounds for one quarter of the stroke, and for the remaining three quarters it varies from 80 pounds to 20 pounds. What we want to know is the mean pressure for the entire stroke. This may be calculated very readily by the aid of Table III. Such calculations are useful in estimating the probable power that may be had from an engine of given dimensions and at different ratios of expansion.

Suppose it is required to find the mean pressure of steam of 100 pounds absolute pressure, cut-off at 6 inches in a cylinder, the stroke of the piston of which is 24 inches: $24 \div 6 = 4$, the ratio of expansion. This (4) will be found in Table III., under the heading *Number*, and opposite it is 2.386. Multiply this by the steam-pressure $2.386 \times 100 = 238.6$. Divide this by the ratio of expansion, 238.6 ÷ 4 = 59.65, the mean pressure in pounds per square inch of steam of 100 pounds absolute pressure cut off at one-quarter stroke.

From the foregoing example the following may be deduced: To find the mean pressure of expanding steam, multiply the hyperbolic logarithm + 1 of the number representing the ratio of expansion by the absolute pressure at cut-off, and divide the product by the ratio of expansion.

To find the ratio of expansion, divide the stroke in inches by the number of inches of the stroke completed when steam is cut off.

To be exact in calculating the mean pressure from the table, the clearance must be taken into account. Thus, if in the example the clearance had been such as in effect to add three quarters of an inch to the length of cylinder on each end, this must be added to the stroke of piston, and also to the distance the piston has moved before cut-off : 24 + .75 = 24.75, 6 + .75 = 6.75, and 24.75 ÷ 6.75 = 3.6, the ratio of expansion. From Table III. the hyperbolic logarithm + 1 of the number 3.6 is 2.281, which multiplied by 100 is 228.1, and this divided by 3.6, equals 63.36 instead of 59.65, as before.

As calculations of this kind are made for approximate results only, it is not generally necessary to take note of clearance, unless it is large, or unless the calculation is made for quite early cut-off ; it may be assumed that what will be gained by clearance will be lost by failure to realize boiler-pressure in the cylinder, and by fall of pressure before cut-off.

From the mean pressure as found in the preceding example not less than 16 pounds absolute back-pressure should be deducted for a non-condensing engine, and not less than 3 pounds for a condensing engine. If there is much compression, a further deduction must be made, according to conditions.

ECONOMY OF EXPANSION.

As will be seen by reference to Table II., the weight of a given volume of steam varies nearly as its pressure; that is, a cubic foot of steam at 40 pounds pressure weighs approximately twice as much as the same volume at 20 pounds pressure. As the weight of steam represents the weight of water that must be evaporated to produce it, the lower the terminal pressure at exhaust-opening in a given cylinder the less the amount of water exhausted as steam. The mean effective pressure is a measure of the work done in the cylinder by the steam; hence it is plain that economy in the use of steam in a steam-engine consists in part in making the mean effective pressure large and the pressure at exhaust-opening small — getting a good deal of work and exhausting a small quantity of steam. This is done by working steam expansively, by cutting off the supply when the piston has made a part only of its stroke, and then getting work from the expanding steam to the end of the stroke. In the preceding example it was seen that with steam of 100 pounds absolute pressure, cut off at one quarter stroke, the mean pressure will be about 60 pounds. This is obtained by filling the cylinder only one quarter full of steam. If the entire cylinder had been filled the mean pressure would have been only 100 pounds. This indicates the direction in which saving is effected, but not the degree of saving. In practice, condensation in the cylinder, and other causes, prevent the full theoretical gain from expansion being realized. But the gain is an important one.

The foregoing will naturally lead to the conclusion that in considering diagrams from cut-off engines we shall expect in a good one to find the initial pressure high compared with the boiler-pressure, the steam-line reasonably straight and cut - off sharp, because these all tend to bring about high mean effective and low terminal pressure ; also, that whatever tends to make the terminal pressure higher than it should be represents waste of steam.

THE ECONOMY OF HIGH PRESSURE.

A brief consideration of the subject will show why the use of high-pressure steam is economical. Taking for example an engine working without expansion, and for simplicity assume that there is no clearance. Assume the engine to be working non-condensing, and the total back-pressure to be 15 pounds—$\frac{3}{10}$ pounds above atmosphere. If in this cylinder steam of 20 pounds absolute pressure is used, the mean effective pressure is $20 - 15 = 5$ pounds. Suppose the cylinder to have a capacity of one cubic foot. We are using, then, at each single stroke of the piston one cubic foot of steam of a pressure of 20 pounds. In Table II. the weight of a cubic foot of steam of this pressure is found to be .0511 pound, and the heat-units per pound 1183.5 ; hence the cubic foot of steam from which the mean effective pressure of 5 pounds has been obtained contained 1183.5 × .0511 = 60.5 heat-units.

Instead of steam of 20 pounds pressure, let steam of 100 pounds be used. The mean effective pressure is 100 − 15 = 85 pounds. The weight of a cubic foot of steam of 100 pounds pressure is .2330 pound, and one pound contains 1213.8 heat-units. Then, as before, 1213.8 × .2330 = 282.8 heat-units used.

In the first instance, 60.5 ÷ 5 = 12.1 heat-units are required for each pound mean effective pressure ; in the second, 282.8 ÷ 85 = 3.3.

The reason for this wide difference in either instance is that the greater part of the total heat of the steam is still in it at the pressure of exhaust (15 pounds), and this is all thrown away. It is only from the heat that is added above exhaust pressure that any can be converted into useful work. As the pressure is increased, a greater per-cent of the total heat is, as will be readily understood, available. If the piston would just move without any effect from the steam, we might go on throwing away a cylinderful at 15 pounds pressure at each half-stroke of the piston, without doing any work whatever.

A clear conception should be had of the fact just referred to, that a large proportion of the heat that goes into the steam used in a steam-engine is required to raise it to the pressure at exhaust, at which pressure no work can be done with it.

The most satisfactory illustration of the economy of the use of high-pressure steam in a cut-off engine is by means of the diagram. Fig. 9 shows it graphically. This is, so far as bounded by the full lines, an actual diagram; above it has been plotted the shaded part

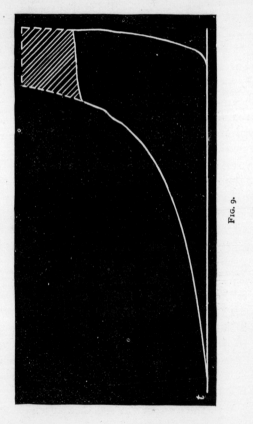

FIG. 9.

precisely as if the whole was a diagram taken at higher steam-pressure. The terminal pressure at t—that is, the pressure of the steam when we are through using it,—is not changed : hence we conclude that, so far as we can judge by the diagram, the work represented by the shaded portion could be done for nothing.*

This subject is an important one: further reference to it will be found under the head of Steam-Engine Economy.

---

* This is on the assumption that steam expands as represented in Chap. VII. If the result were worked out from Table II. it would be slightly different. But we do not know with certainty that it would be any nearer correct. For all practical purposes this presentation may be accepted, and in all consideration of diagrams that follow steam will be supposed to expand according to Mariotte's law.

CHAPTER VIII.

COMPUTING THE HORSE-POWER.

FINDING THE MEAN EFFECTIVE PRESSURE.

FOR measuring from the diagram the mean effective pressure, we may consider that the upper line—that is, all the inclosing lines of the figure that are traced while the piston is moving ahead—represents the pressure moving it, and that the opposing force is represented by the lower line traced while the piston is returning. A little reflection will show that the opposing force is actually represented by the lower line of a diagram simultaneously taken from the other end of the cylinder, but no error will arise in the process of finding the mean effective pressure by considering the diagram from each end complete in itself. What we want is to measure the mean or average distance apart of the upper and lower line of the diagram by the scale of the spring used : this will be the mean effective pressure—a factor in calculating the indicated horse-power. This is all that is required, except where expansion is carried so far that the expansion-line crosses the line of counter-pressure, or when compression is carried to such an extent that a loop is formed at the termination of the return and beginning of the forward stroke. An instance of the kind first mentioned—which is only likely to be met with in the case of a non-condensing engine cutting off short, as when lightly loaded—is represented in Fig. 11, page 50; the

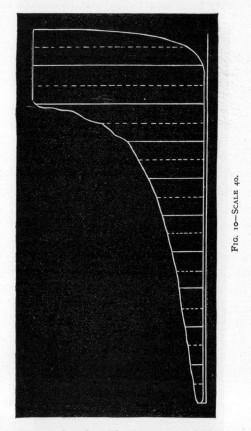

FIG. 10—SCALE 40.

second mentioned, of still rarer occurrence, is represented in Fig. 6, page 33.

The amount of work done on one side of the piston may differ materially from that done on the other

4

side, and almost invariably does differ to some extent. For this reason, in finding the horse-power developed, it is necessary to measure diagrams from both ends of

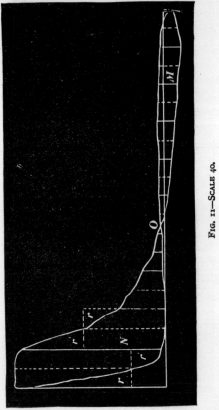

FIG. 11—SCALE 40.

the cylinder, when the average mean effective pressure of the two will be that required.

Altogether, the most accurate and expeditious way

to measure the mean effective pressure represented by the diagram is by means of the planimeter, or averaging instrument; but as such an instrument is not always at hand, it may by careful working be very accurately done by dividing the diagram into a number of equal parts, say ten, as in Fig. 10, measuring the height of each division, adding these measurements together, and dividing the sum by the number of divisions. The only reason for making the number of divisions 10 is for convenience; some prefer to make the number 20, as tending to greater accuracy. The height of each division can be measured by a scale of pounds, the measurements added together and divided by 10, the result appearing in pounds; or the measurements can be made by a scale of inches, the sum multiplied by the scale of the spring, and divided by 10, giving the result as before. As tending to greater accuracy, however, it is advisable to make the measurements continuous. For this purpose a strip of paper is used, which is carried from one division to another, the measure of each being pricked or marked beyond the preceding one, so that the distance from the end of the strip to the last mark will represent the sum of the 10 measurements.

In Fig. 10 this distance is 7.075 inches, the number of divisions 10, and the scale of the indicator-spring 40; hence the mean effective pressure is

$$\frac{7.075 \times 40}{10} = 28.3 \text{ pounds.}$$

THE HORSE-POWER.

The data required to find the indicated horse-power from a pair of diagrams are: The diameter of cylinder, stroke of piston, diameter of piston-rod, revolutions per minute, and scale of indicator-spring. In this instance the diameter of cylinder is 18.3 inches, stroke of piston 42 inches, diameter of piston-rod $3\frac{1}{8}$ inches, revolutions per minute 72, and the scale of spring $1'' =$ 40 pounds. The mean net area of the cylinder (the total area less one half the area of piston-rod) is 259.18 inches, and the piston-speed 504 feet per minute; so that if the mean effective pressure of the diagram from the other end is the same as this, the indicated horse-power is

$$\frac{259.18 \times 28.3 \times 504}{33,000} = 112.$$

Fig. 11 represents a case in which the pressure falls, by expansion, below the line of counter-pressure, crossing the latter at O, from which point to the end of the stroke it is plain that the pressure urging the piston forward is less than that resisting its progress. To get the mean effective pressure in such an instance, it is evident that the resistance indicated by the part M of the diagram must be deducted from the forward pressure indicated by the part N. This is conveniently done by measuring the combined height of the 4 divisions included in N, similarly measuring the 6 divisions of M, and subtracting the latter from the former. The combined height of the 4 divisions of N is $2\frac{5}{8}''$, and of the 6 divisions of M $\frac{7}{8}''$: then $2\frac{5}{8}'' - \frac{7}{8}''$

$= 1\frac{3}{4}''$, which multiplied by 40 and divided by 10 gives a mean effective pressure of 7 pounds.

It should not be inferred that measuring the divisions of the diagram at their centres, as on the broken lines, will always be correct. It would be more nearly true to say that it will never be correct. It is the mean height of each division that is required, and the eye will generally determine whether this will result from measuring at the centre. In Fig. 10, measuring the height of the 10 divisions on the centre (broken) lines will give a mean effective pressure of 28.81 pounds, or about $\frac{1}{2}$ pound too much; and in Fig. 11 it will give 6.5 pounds, an amount too small by more than 7 per cent. Why this is so will be better understood by an examination of the first and second divisions of Fig. 11, in each of which it is evident that the parts r' that ought to be measured, but are not included in a measurement on the centre line, are not equal with the parts r that are measured, but ought not to be. An examination of other divisions of both Figs. 10 and 11 will afford additional evidence that the practice of drawing the centre lines only and taking their measurements as conclusive is likely — almost certain—to lead to error. By drawing the boundary lines as well as the centre line of each division, then when any doubt exists, drawing the short horizontal lines (as near r, r'), the spaces r, r' can be compared by the eye, after a little practice, with great exactness. Additional short horizontal lines can be drawn above

or below these to indicate the point to which to measure to equalize the spaces, or where the case presents
difficulties a division can be subdivided any number of
times, and the height averaged in a way similar to that
in which the height of the diagram is averaged.

HORSE-POWER FOR ONE POUND MEAN EFFECTIVE PRESSURE.

When a number of diagrams are to be calculated, the
horse-power for one pound mean effective pressure
may be computed, and this multiplied by the mean
effective pressure of the different diagrams will give
the horse-power of each. It is simply a shorter way
to deal with several diagrams. Thus in the preceding
instance the horse-power for one pound pressure would
be

$$\frac{259.18 \times 1 \times 504}{33,000} = 3.96,$$

which multiplied by the mean effective pressure—3.96
$\times$ 28.3 = 212—gives the horse-power the same as
before.

CHAPTER IX.

THE THEORETICAL CURVE.

REASONS FOR ESTABLISHING IT.

IF there were neither loss nor gain of heat by the steam in the cylinder of a steam-engine, nor leakage of the piston or valves, or other disturbing causes, the expansion-curve that would be traced by the indicator could be predetermined very nearly. But because there is a loss of heat, and because the piston and valves are in practice never absolutely tight, the expansion-curve departs in a degree, greater or less, from the curve that would be established from theoretical considerations alone. For the purpose of determining the extent of this departure the theoretical curve is drawn upon the diagram and compared with the actual expansion-curve. The curve most commonly employed for this purpose is that of the hyperbola—the Mariotte curve. From what was said in Chapter VII. it will be understood that this curve is not the one that would be traced by the indicator under absolutely perfect conditions in the cylinder of the engine, but it is near enough so for all practical purposes, and its close approximation by the diagram is, to a certain extent, evidence of good practice and conditions. But, as will be explained further on, this should not be blindly taken as being so, as it may indicate quite the reverse of good conditions. To state it in another way, when the actual and theoretical curves are found to agree

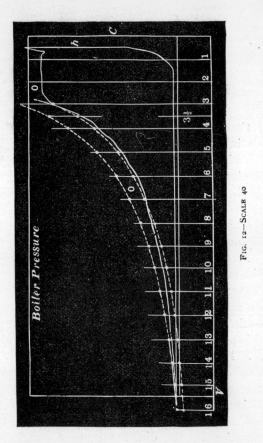

Fig. 12—Scale 40

substantially, it is strong presumptive evidence of good conditions.

It is only necessary for the establishment of this

curve to consider that the pressure of steam varies inversely as its volume, or the space it occupies, from which consideration any desired number of points in the curve can be readily determined. Since all pressure must be measured from vacuum, and the clearance must be considered, the line of vacuum, V (Fig. 12), and the clearance line, C, are laid off, the former at a distance below the atmospheric line representing by the scale of the indicator-spring 14.7 pounds, and the latter at a distance, h, from the beginning of the diagram, representing the added length of the cylinder that would equal the capacity of the clearance-space on one end. Suppose, as in the present instance, the clearance-space (which must include *all* the space that will be occupied by steam with the piston at the end of the stroke) is found to equal 4 per cent of the piston-displacement, which is represented by the length of the diagram; the distance, h, will then be 4 per cent of that length.

There are different ways of establishing points in this curve, one of which is as follows: Draw on the diagram vertical lines, starting from the clearance-line, an equal distance apart, and number them as shown. In spacing these lines it is not necessary to pay any attention to coming out even at the end of the diagram; one or more lines, as 16, may be quite beyond the diagram. Generally speaking, the more numerous the lines the more easily and accurately the curve may be drawn, but beyond this the number of lines is quite immaterial.

POINTS FROM WHICH TO DRAW THE THEORETICAL CURVE.

The theoretical curve may be drawn from any point in the real curve, the only precaution necessary being to select a point at which it is known that the steam and exhaust valves are closed. Generally it is better to draw the curve from a point representing a piston position either just before the exhaust-valve opens, or just after the steam-valve has closed. In Fig. 12 the curve is drawn in broken lines from both these points. Selecting some point, as where the 14 line crosses the real expansion-curve, measure the pressure from vacuum up to this point. The scale of the spring is 40, and the pressure is 18 pounds. The number of volumes is, according to the unit adopted and represented by the distance apart of the vertical lines, 14; hence to find the pressure on any other line, multiply this pressure by the number of the line, and divide the product by the number of the line upon which it is desired to determine the pressure. Thus $18 \times 14 = 252$, which, divided by 5, equals 50.4 pounds, the pressure to be set off on line 5. By setting off the pressures on all the lines and connecting the points, as shown, the curve is established.

Sometimes, near the point of cut-off, it will be found difficult to connect the points satisfactorily. When this is the case, another line, as $3\frac{1}{2}$, may be drawn, and another point in the curve set off. In drawing the curve from the intersection of line 3, the same general plan is to be pursued; that is, multiply the pressure on that line by 3, and divide by the numbers of the other lines to find the pressures on them.

It will be understood that it is not necessary that a scale of pounds be used at all; or, if it be, it need not necessarily be the scale of the spring, as all that need be considered is that the product of the distance horizontally from C and the height from the vacuum-line V of all points or parts of the curve are equal. Thus, if at a distance of 2 inches from C the pressure is 50 pounds, at 3 inches it will be

$$\frac{2 \times 50}{3} = 33\tfrac{1}{3} \text{ pounds}$$

$$(2 \times 50 = 100, \quad \text{and} \quad 3 \times 33\tfrac{1}{3} = 100).$$

It is of course necessary to establish the vacuum-line by the scale of the spring used in taking the diagram, but this may be done by dividing 14.7 (or any number of pounds corresponding to the observed pressure of the atmosphere) by the scale of the spring: the quotient will be in inches. In the present instance the distance of this line below the atmospheric line is 14.7 ÷ 40 = .3675″—a little less than $\tfrac{3}{8}$ inch. Having established the vacuum-line, any scale of equal parts may be used in setting off the points in the curve.

If it is desired to show graphically how much higher the pressure is at the end of the stroke than it should be, the curve drawn as from the intersection of line 3 will accomplish the purpose. But if it is desired to show how much more work might have been done with the steam accounted for by the indicator at the end of the stroke, then the curve should be drawn as from the intersection of line 14. In this instance, if the steam line is continued till it cuts the upper curve, the space

O inclosed above the actual curve will represent this work.

In selecting a point near cut-off from which to draw

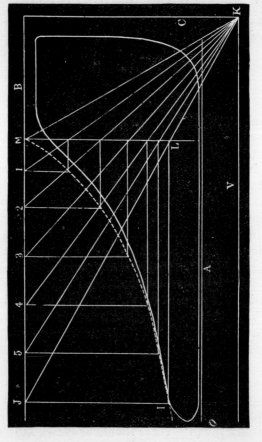

Fig. 13—Scale 40.

the expansion-curve it should be concluded that steam is not cut off until the flexure of the curve changes.

Thus in diagram 14, for instance, the rounded corner near cut-off is occasioned by the contraction of the port-area while the valve is closing. At S the flexure or direction of the curve changes from concave upward to concave downward : we conclude that steam continued to enter the cylinder until this point in the stroke. In diagrams from engines in which the valve-motion closes the steam-port slowly the cut-off will be found at a point much later in the stroke than we might conclude from a casual inspection, and after a very material fall of pressure. Diagrams from loco-motive-engines at high speed show this peculiarity in a marked degree.

GEOMETRICAL METHOD OF FINDING POINTS IN THE THEO-RETICAL CURVE.

The following method of locating points in the theoretical curve will doubtless be preferred by many to the preceding one : In Fig. 13 select any point, as I, in the actual curve, and from this point draw a vertical line to J on line B. The line B may be, as it is here, the line of boiler-pressure ; but this is not material : it may be drawn at any convenient height near the top of the diagram. From J draw the diagonal to K, K being the intersection of the vacuum and clearance lines, and from I draw IL parallel with the atmospheric line and at right angles to IJ. From L, the point of intersection of the diagonal JK and the horizontal line IL, draw the vertical line LM. The point M is the theoretical point of cut-off, and LM the cut-off line. Fix upon any number of points, 1, 2, 3, etc., on line B, and from these points draw diagonals to *K*. From the intersection of these diagonals with *LM* draw horizontal lines, and from 1, 2, 3, etc., vertical lines. Where these lines meet will be points in the theoretical curve.

LOCATING THE CLEARANCE-LINE ON THE DIAGRAM.

The clearance-space—such part of it as is embraced in the ports—is from its irregularity difficult of measurement. If the valve is blocked against the face, the engine placed on the dead-centre, and the clearance-space filled with water, the quantity being carefully weighed, the space it occupies will be known. Water at a temperature of 60° will occupy a space of 27.7 cubic inches per pound. Say that $6\frac{1}{2}$ pounds are required to fill the clearance-space in a $16'' \times 32''$ cylinder, the cubic inches of space occupied by the water will be $27.7 \times 6.5 = 180.05$ cubic inches. The area of a $16''$ cylinder is 201.068 inches, and the space swept through by the piston in a single stroke is $201.068 \times 32 = 6434.176$ cubic inches; the clearance is $180.05 \div 6434.176 = .028$ of the displacement. If the diagram is $4\frac{1}{4}$ inches long the distance *h*, Fig. 12, will be $4.25 \times .028 = .119$ inch.

PROFESSOR SWEET'S PLAN FOR MEASURING CLEARANCE.

The following remarkably simple plan for determining clearance was communicated to the *American Machinist* by Professor John E. Sweet. He says: " See that the piston and valves are made tight, and the valves disconnected; arrange to fill the clearance-space with water through the indicator-holes, or through

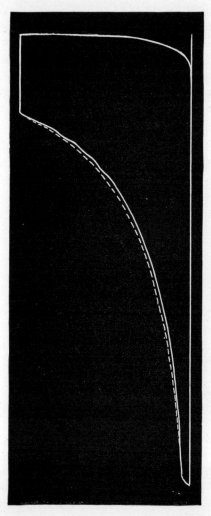

FIG. 12½—SCALE 40.

holes drilled for the purpose. Turn the engine on the dead-centre; make marks on the cross-head and guides; weigh a pail of water, and from it fill the clearance-space. Weigh the remaining water so as to determine how much is used. Then weigh out exactly the same amount of water [as is used], turn the engine off the centre, pour in the second charge of water, and turn the engine back till the water comes to the same point that it did in the first instance. Make another mark on the cross-head and guide, and the distance between these marks is exactly what you really wish to know; that is, it is just what piston-travel equals the clearance. . . . If it takes 1 pound of water to fill this space and to admit another pound, the piston must be moved 1 inch: then the clearance bears the same relation to the capacity of the cylinder as 1 inch bears to the stroke of the piston. Thus, under these circumstances, in an engine of 10 inches stroke, it would be said to have 10 per cent clearance."

It may be added that, considering the length of the indicator-diagram as representing the stroke of the piston drawn to a scale, it is only necessary to lay off this 1 inch (or whatever the distance may be) on the same scale to establish the clearance-line on the diagram.

It was remarked near the beginning of this chapter that it was evidence of good conditions when the theoretical and actual expansion curves were found to agree, or very nearly so. Fig. 12½ shows reasonable compliance in this respect—in fact much better than the average; such as might be expected from a cylinder not much less than 16 inches diameter, working with piston and valves tight.

CHAPTER X.

MEASURING FROM THE DIAGRAM THE STEAM EXHAUSTED.

STEAM EXHAUSTED PER HOUR.

THE amount of *steam* in the cylinder at any point in the stroke can be measured from the diagram, but unfortunately the water present that entered the cylinder as steam cannot be so measured. For this reason the steam actually entering the cylinder cannot be determined by the use of the indicator, but measuring that accounted for by the indicator we know that a *less* quantity could not have been used; in fact, we know that more—sometimes much more—is used. In measuring the steam accounted for by the indicator it is generally advisable to select some point in the stroke just previous to the opening of the exhaust-valve, when the displacement of the piston in cubic feet up to that point, *plus* the clearance-space, multiplied by the weight of a cubic foot of steam of the pressure at the point selected, will give the weight of steam present. From this must be deducted the steam saved by the closing of the exhaust-valve before the end of the stroke, the remainder being the steam expended. Instead of determining the steam used per stroke, it is better to calculate the amount used per hour. In **Fig.** 14, which represents a diagram from an engine with a $10'' \times 18''$ cylinder at 100 revolutions, 30 spring, a convenient plan is represented. The lines, x, y, are drawn

at a distance equal to the clearance-space from each
end of the diagram. Measuring the pressure (from
vacuum) on line *y*, it is found to be 27.5 pounds; and
since *y* is at a distance from the end of the diagram
equal to the clearance-space, it follows that the space
occupied by steam at this point in the stroke is just

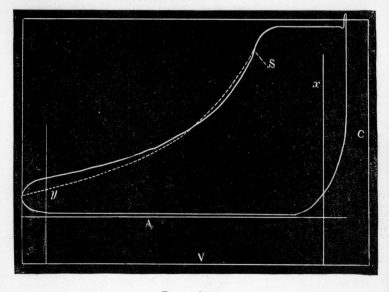

FIG. 14—SCALE 30.

equal to the piston-displacement for a single stroke.
The mean net area of the piston is, say, 77 inches, so
the displacement is $77 \times 18 = 1386$ inches. The number of single strokes per minute is 200, and per hour
$200 \times 60 = 12,000$; hence the displacement of the
piston per hour is

$$\frac{12,000 \times 1386}{1728} = 9625$$

cubic feet.

The weight of a cubic foot of steam at a pressure of 27.5 is, according to Table II., .0695 pound (found by adding the weight at 27 and at 28 pounds together, and dividing by 2): so the weight of steam per hour in the cylinder at this point in the stroke is $9625 \times .0695 = 668.93$ pounds.

The process so far should be clearly understood: hence the repetition that, by measuring the pressure at y, distance from that end of the diagram just equal to the clearance-space C, the volume at that point (y) will be just equal to the piston - displacement; we have added the clearance at C, but have cut off an equal distance at y.

This 668.93 pounds is the weight of the steam per hour in the cylinder, as found by calculating it at some convenient point, y, on the expansion-curve. And this would be the weight of the steam exhausted per hour were it not for the fact that it is not exhausted down to vacuum, from which the pressure is calculated. Some of it is saved in the clearance-space upon the return of the piston, and this amount is increased by the exhaust-valve closing before the end of the return stroke. Line x is at a distance equal to the clearance from the end of the diagram, and the clearance is 7 per cent of the piston-displacement: hence if we calculate the steam saved per hour from the point where x crosses the compression-curve the volume will be just 14 per cent of the piston-displacement—that is, $9625 \times .14 = 1347.5$ cubic feet per hour.

The pressure of the steam saved, measured from vacuum up to where x crosses the compression-curve, is
22 pounds, and from Table II. the weight of a cubic
foot of steam at that pressure is .0561 pound: hence the
steam saved per hour is $1347.5 \times .0561 = 75.59$ pounds.
The steam, then, actually exhausted is $668.93 - 75.59$
$= 593.34$ pounds per hour.

The mean effective pressure is 29.6 pounds, and the
piston-speed 300 feet per minute; the indicated horse-
power is

$$\frac{77 \times 29.6 \times 300}{33,000} = 20.7,$$

and the steam accounted for by the indicator per horse-
power per hour is $593.34 \div 20.7 = 28.6$ pounds. The
steam actually used was of course considerably in excess of this.

It is not essential that the points x and y be taken
at a distance equal to the clearance-line from the ends
of the diagram, or that they be at equal distance from
each end: the process consists in finding the volume,
including clearance, at some point previous to exhaust-
opening, and from the volume and pressure calculating
the weight of steam, for convenience by the hour, and
similarly finding the weight saved from some point in
the compression-curve. Subtracting the latter quantity from the former gives the weight actually exhausted. When the points x and y can be conveniently located as represented, as they generally can be,
it shortens the operation.

It has been previously intimated that it was not always an easy matter to determine by the diagram how

much of the variation between the actual and the theoretical curve was due to condensation and re-evaporation,
and how much to leakages by valves and piston. In
Fig. 14 it will be noticed that the actual curve falls below the theoretical soon after the steam-valve has
closed. This is generally the case in an unjacketed
cylinder, and is rationally enough accounted for by
condensation in the cylinder, the difference in temperature between the walls of the cylinder and the steam
being greater than later in the stroke, and hence the
conditions favorable for rapid condensation. But if
the piston or exhaust-valve leak, the leakage will be
greatest at this time, owing to the higher pressure of
steam, and this may be taken to account for the fall in
pressure. The real curve soon rises and crosses the
theoretical curve, which may be accounted for by the
re-evaporation of water by the excess of heat after
the fall in pressure. But this increase of steam may
also be accounted for by leakage of the steam-valve,
which would naturally increase in amount as the pressure fell, while if the piston and exhaust-valve, either
or both, leaked, the leakage by them would be correspondingly diminished.

It will be noticed that the pressure rises very rapidly
towards the end of the stroke, so much so as to point
to the probability of a leaky steam-valve, which, it may
be as well to state, was found to be the case.

It may readily be seen that the leakage of valves and
piston may be such as to assist in producing a more
nearly correct expansion-curve than would result if
they were tight, for which reason hasty conclusions as
to the economy of an engine should not be drawn from

the quality of this curve, nor from the steam accounted for by the indicator.

The following table, prepared by E. W. Thompson for the *American Machinist*, is in accordance with the plan for computing steam-consumption in use by the

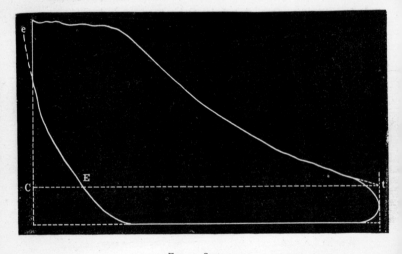

FIG. 15—SCALE 40.

Buckeye Engine Company. The plan is illustrated in Fig. 15. To use the table the mean effective pressure must be known, but the horse-power, or the dimensions of the cylinder even, need not be known. Draw a vertical line at each end of the diagram exactly defining its length, and continue the expansion-curve guided by the eye to *t*, as if the exhaust had not opened. From *t*

draw the line tC parallel with the atmospheric line.
Measure the terminal pressure at t (from vacuum), and
find in the table, page 72, the number corresponding
to it.   In the table the numbers under T. P. represent
the terminal pressure in pounds, and the figures at the
head, 1, 2, 3, etc., tenths of a pound.   If the terminal
pressure is, say, 16 pounds, in the column against 16
and under 0. is 567.360, the required number.   If the
terminal pressure is, say, 20.6 pounds, against 20 and
under 6 is 719.558, the number.

Divide the number thus found by the mean effective
pressure : the quotient will be the steam accounted for
by the indicator per horse-power per hour, uncorrected
for clearance and compression.   To make this correc-
tion multiply by the length of the line tE, and divide
by the length of the line tC.

It will sometimes happen that the maximum compression will not be as high as the terminal pressure.
In that case tE will be longer than tC.   When this
occurs the compression-curve must be extended by the
aid of the eye, as indicated at e, and E will be outside
the diagram.   When the maximum compression is
higher than the terminal pressure tE will be shorter
than tC.

In Fig. 14 the terminal pressure is 28.3 pounds, and
the mean effective pressure 44.6.   In the table under
3 and against 28 is 969.813, which divided by 44.6 =
21.74.   This is the steam-consumption uncorrected for
clearance and compression.   The length of tE is 3.2
inches, and of tC 3.7 inches; 21.74 multiplied by 3.2
and divided by 3.7 = 18.8, the pounds of dry steam
exhausted per horse-power per hour.

THOMPSON'S COMPUTATION TABLE.

T.P.	0	1	2	3	4	5	6	7	8	9
3	117.300	121.015	124.717	128.406	132.083	135.748	139.399	143.075	146.665	150.279
4	153.880	157.514	161.137	164.750	168.353	171.945	175.527	179.098	182.659	186.210
5	189.750	193.336	196.914	200.483	204.044	207.598	211.142	214.679	218.208	221.728
6	225.240	228.799	232.351	235.897	239.417	242.970	246.497	250.017	253.531	257.039
7	260.540	264.036	267.506	271.071	274.570	278.063	281.550	285.031	288.506	291.976
8	295.440	298.922	302.400	305.872	309.338	312.800	316.256	319.708	323.154	326.594
9	330.030	333.488	336.941	340.389	343.833	347.273	350.707	354.137	357.563	360.984
10	364.400	367.842	371.280	374.714	378.144	381.570	384.992	388.410	391.824	395.234
11	398.640	402.064	405.485	408.902	412.315	415.725	417.131	422.534	425.933	429.328
12	432.720	436.120	439.517	442.911	446.301	449.688	453.071	456.451	459.828	463.200
13	466.570	469.950	473.326	476.699	480.068	483.435	486.798	490.159	493.516	496.869
14	500.220	503.596	506.968	510.338	513.706	517.070	520.432	523.790	527.146	530.500
15	533.850	537.213	540.573	543.930	547.285	550.638	553.987	557.334	560.679	564.011
16	567.360	570.713	574.063	577.411	580.757	584.100	587.441	590.780	594.115	597.449
17	600.780	604.109	607.435	610.759	614.081	617.400	620.717	624.031	627.343	630.653
18	633.960	637.265	640.567	643.867	647.165	650.460	653.753	657.043	660.331	663.617
19	666.900	670.200	673.498	676.703	680.086	683.378	686.666	689.953	693.238	696.520
20	699.800	703.098	706.394	709.688	712.980	716.270	719.558	722.844	726.128	729.410
21	732.690	735.958	739.244	742.518	745.790	749.060	752.328	755.594	758.858	762.120
22	765.380	768.660	771.938	775.215	778.490	781.763	785.034	788.303	791.570	794.836
23	798.100	801.362	804.622	807.881	811.138	814.303	817.646	820.807	824.146	827.334
24	830.640	833.908	837.175	840.440	843.703	846.965	850.225	853.484	856.741	859.906
25	863.250	866.502	869.753	873.002	876.249	879.495	882.739	885.082	889.223	892.462
26	895.700	898.936	902.171	905.404	908.635	911.865	915.023	918.300	921.545	924.768
27	927.990	931.201	934.429	937.646	940.831	944.075	947.287	950.498	953.707	956.914
28	960.120	963.352	966.583	969.813	973.041	976.268	979.493	982.717	985.939	989.160
29	992.380	995.598	998.815	1002.031	1005.245	1008.458	1011.669	1014.879	1018.087	1021.294
30	1024.500	1027.704	1030.007	1034.109	1037.309	1040.508	1043.725	1046.901	1050.095	1053.288
31	1056.480	1059.670	1062.859	1066.047	1069.233	1072.418	1075.661	1078.783	1081.963	1085.142

THOMPSON'S COMPUTATION TABLE—*Continued.*

T.P.	0	1	2	3	4	5	6	7	8	9
32	1088.320	1091.528	1094.736	1097.942	1101.146	1104.350	1107.552	1110.754	1113.954	1117.152
33	1120.350	1123.546	1126.742	1129.936	1133.128	1136.420	1139.510	1142.700	1145.888	1149.074
34	1152.260	1155.444	1158.628	1161.810	1164.990	1168.170	1171.348	1174.526	1177.702	1180.876
35	1184.050	1187.222	1190.394	1193.564	1196.732	1199.900	1203.066	1206.232	1209.396	1212.558
36	1215.720	1218.917	1222.112	1225.307	1228.500	1231.693	1234.884	1238.075	1241.264	1244.453
37	1247.640	1250.827	1254.012	1257.197	1260.380	1263.563	1266.744	1269.925	1273.104	1276.283
38	1279.460	1282.637	1285.812	1288.987	1292.160	1295.333	1298.504	1301.675	1304.844	1308.013
39	1311.180	1314.347	1317.512	1320.677	1323.840	1327.003	1330.164	1333.325	1336.484	1339.643
40	1342.800	1345.957	1349.112	1352.267	1355.420	1358.573	1361.724	1364.875	1368.024	1371.173
41	1374.320	1377.407	1380.612	1383.757	1386.900	1390.043	1393.184	1396.325	1399.464	1402.603
42	1405.740	1408.877	1412.012	1415.147	1418.280	1421.413	1424.544	1427.675	1430.804	1433.933
43	1437.060	1440.230	1443.398	1446.566	1449.734	1452.900	1456.066	1459.230	1462.394	1465.558
44	1468.720	1471.882	1475.042	1478.202	1481.362	1484.520	1487.678	1490.834	1493.990	1497.146
45	1500.300	1503.454	1506.606	1509.758	1512.910	1516.060	1519.210	1522.359	1525.506	1528.654
46	1531.800	1534.946	1538.090	1541.234	1544.378	1547.520	1550.662	1553.802	1556.942	1560.082
47	1563.220	1566.358	1569.494	1572.630	1575.766	1578.900	1582.034	1585.166	1588.298	1591.430
48	1594.560	1597.690	1600.818	1603.946	1607.074	1610.200	1613.326	1616.450	1619.574	1622.698
49	1625.820	1628.942	1632.062	1635.182	1638.302	1641.420	1644.538	1647.654	1650.770	1653.886
50	1657.000	1660.114	1663.226	1666.338	1669.450	1672.560	1675.670	1678.778	1681.886	1684.994
51	1688.100	1691.206	1694.310	1697.414	1700.518	1703.620	1706.722	1709.822	1712.922	1716.022
52	1719.120	1722.218	1725.314	1728.410	1731.506	1734.600	1737.604	1740.786	1743.878	1746.970
53	1750.060	1753.150	1756.238	1759.327	1762.414	1765.500	1768.586	1771.670	1774.754	1777.838
54	1780.920	1784.002	1787.082	1790.162	1793.242	1796.320	1799.398	1802.474	1805.550	1808.626
55	1811.700	1814.829	1817.957	1821.084	1824.211	1827.338	1830.463	1833.588	1836.713	1839.837
56	1842.960	1846.083	1849.205	1852.326	1855.447	1858.568	1861.687	1864.806	1867.925	1871.043
57	1874.160	1877.277	1880.393	1883.508	1886.623	1889.738	1892.851	1895.964	1899.077	1902.189
58	1905.300	1908.411	1911.521	1914.630	1917.739	1920.848	1923.955	1927.062	1930.169	1933.275
59	1936.380	1939.485	1942.589	1945.692	1948.795	1951.898	1954.999	1958.100	1961.201	1964.301
60	1967.400	1970.499	1973.597	1976.694	1979.791	1982.888	1985.983	1989.078	1992.173	1995.267

CHAPTER XI.

CONDENSING ENGINES.

DIAGRAMS FROM A STEAM-JACKETED CYLINDER.

So far as computing the horse-power is concerned, it is immaterial whether the diagram is from a condensing or from a non-condensing engine, the determination of the distance apart of the upper and lower lines being all that is required in either case. But in a condensing engine it is of interest to measure separately the work done above and below the atmosphere, so as to determine how much of all the work done to credit the condenser with. The pair of diagrams represented in Fig. 16 will serve to illustrate this, besides being interesting in other respects. They are from both ends of a cylinder $27'' \times 36''$, at a piston-speed of 90 feet per minute; cylinder completely steam-jacketed, including the ends. The clearance is .026 of the piston-displacement. The approximate theoretical curve is drawn on one diagram from a point near release, and on the other from a point just after cut-off. The mean effective pressure of the right-hand diagram is 44.94, and of the left-hand 42.06 pounds, an average of 43.5 pounds. The diameter of the piston-rod is 3.5 inches, and the mean net area of the piston 567.75 inches, so the horse-power for each pound mean effective pressure is

$$\frac{567.75 \times 1 \times 90}{33,000} = 1.548.$$

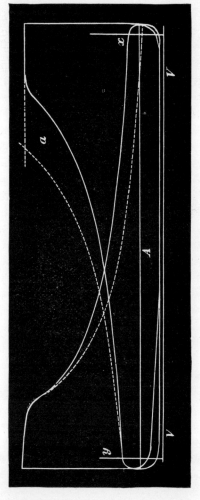

Fig. 16—Scale 60.

The pressure exerted below the atmosphere is by the right-hand diagram 10.76, and by the left 11.82 pounds, an average of 11.29 pounds,—nearly 26 per cent of the total mean effective pressure exerted. The indicated horse-power is 63.33, and the water per horse-power per hour accounted for by the indicator is 18.6 pounds.

Of the prominent features of these diagrams the admission-lines are good, as well as the steam-lines and cut-off, all of which is, of course, easy to bring about at the slow piston-speed. The expansion-curves show a remarkable departure from the theoretical curves, which is not easily accounted for if the steam-jackets prevent initial condensation. If, however, there was a good deal of initial condensation, the heat from the jackets may have re-evaporated the most of the water, and the increase of terminal pressure may have been due to this; or it may have been due in part to the evaporation of water that entered the cylinder *as water*, and in part to leakage of steam-valves. Whatever it is due to, it represents a loss that may in part be seen by considering that the space *a* on the right-hand diagram represents work that might under better conditions have been done by the steam that was present in the cylinder at the opening of the exhaust-valves. Measuring this space, it amounts to an addition of seven pounds to the mean effective pressure ; 15.5 per cent more work might have been done by the steam exhausted. The terminal pressure is about 40 per cent higher than it ought to be. It is not at all probable that such an amount of water entered with the steam, so that the most of the rise in pressure must be attributed to initial condensation and evaporation later in the stroke, and to leakage of steam-valves.

In calculating the efficiency of a condensing engine, so far as the work done below the atmosphere is concerned, it is essential to know the vacuum in the condenser; for, as in a non-condensing engine, the back-pressure that should be accounted against the cylinder is the difference between the line of counter-pressure and the atmospheric line, so in a condensing engine it is the difference between the line of counter-pressure and an imaginary line representing the pressure maintained in the condenser. Calculated in this way, under the same conditions otherwise, the back-pressure in a condensing engine will be somewhat greater than in a non-condensing engine. In this instance the vacuum by gauge was 25 inches, in pounds 12.27. As the average pressure below atmosphere is 11.29, a small fraction of a pound being lost by compression, the result in this respect is very good indeed. This small amount of back-pressure would have been reduced by about $\frac{1}{4}$ pound if the exhaust-opening on the end represented by the left-hand diagram had been a little earlier and more ample. Of course, at higher speeds the back-pressure would, with the same valves and valve-motion, have been increased; in fact, at high piston-speed it is not practicable to make the exhaust-openings so ample as to result in so little back-pressure as shown here. Altogether, these diagrams are excellent ones below the atmospheric line; good ones above, so far as admission-lines, steam-lines, and release are concerned; but decidedly poor ones so far as the expansion-curve has to do with their quality

DIAGRAMS FROM AN ENGINE CONDENSING AND NON-CONDENSING COMPARED.

The diagrams Fig. 17 represent graphically the effect of adding a condenser to a non-condensing engine. Both diagrams were taken on the same paper, as engraved—one with the condenser in use, and the other with the exhaust turned into the atmosphere. The fact that they were so taken, and that the load remained constant, makes it easy to compare them, and also makes the comparison more satisfactory. The engine from which they were taken is $18'' \times 36''$, and at the time of taking the diagrams the revolutions were 109, boiler-pressure 62 pounds, vacuum (by gauge) $24''$, 40 spring. The clearance is four per cent of the piston-displacement.

The mean effective pressure of the two diagrams is the same—28.32 pounds. The non-condensing diagram shows the terminal pressure to have been 24 pounds, the load—142 horse-power—being too much for good economy calculated from the diagram ; or, to state it another way, and more correctly, the steam-pressure was too low for the load. The dry steam accounted for by the indicator was 25 pounds per horse-power per hour. The result with 20 pounds higher boiler-pressure would have been quite different.

Comparing this with the condensing diagram, the terminal pressure by the latter is 14.5 pounds and the dry steam exhausted 16.7 pounds per horse-power per hour : a remarkably good result for this steam-pressure and poor vacuum, for which, of course, the engine was not responsible. Looking at the general features of the condensing diagram, the amount of compression is quite remarkable. This is brought about by the large

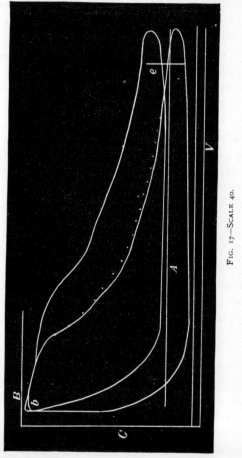

FIG. 17—SCALE 40.

amount of inside lap. The inside lap—$\frac{5}{8}''$ with $\frac{3}{4}''$ outside lap—probably accounts in part for a little more back-pressure than might be expected, but from the fact that the exhaust-pipe is badly arranged, it is not certain how much of this back-pressure is due to the lack of exhaust-lead, and how much to the arrangement of the pipe. (The line nearest the vacuum-line V represents the pressure in the condenser, and is the one from which the back-pressure should be measured.) The faulty arrangement of the exhaust-pipe referred to is in running it down direct from the cylinder (the pipe is 6″ diameter) for a short distance and then returning at an acute angle direct from the pipe leading down, without any enlargement or easing off of the bend whatever. Assuming that this bend in the exhaust-pipe is the principal cause of back-pressure, it is still probable that an earlier opening of the exhaust-valve would reduce it slightly, since it would afford more time for the steam to pass the stricture in the pipe. Reducing the inside lap would correspondingly reduce the compression, but would probably leave sufficient to satisfactorily cushion the piston. The exhaust-lap might probably be reduced to $\frac{1}{2}$″ or $\frac{3}{8}$″, and then a little more steam-lead given to help up the compression, with satisfactory results, the slightly-rounded corner at b indicating that a little more steam-lead would do no harm otherwise. If this should result in a pound less average back-pressure, it would make a decidedly good diagram still a little better. It is needless to say that the first thing that *ought* to be done is to rearrange the exhaust-pipe so as to get rid of the sharp bend.

Points in the theoretical curve of the condensing diagram are indicated, beginning on the actual curve at the vertical line *e*. It will be seen that the theoretical and actual curves agree exactly at each end, but that the latter falls a little below the former at the middle. This is what should be with ordinary dry steam, unjacketed cylinder and tight valves. The cut-off is reasonably sharp for the piston-speed, and the steam-line good. Larger ports would give a little straighter steam-line, but there is the question if the loss otherwise would not more than balance any gain that would result.

The distance of the atmospheric line *A*, below the point of terminal pressure of the non-condensing diagram, is almost exactly equal to the distance of the line of condenser-pressure below the terminal pressure of the condensing diagrams; hence, if the steam escape with equal facility in both instances, the back-pressure of the two diagrams should be equal. But the back-pressure, as usual, is the greatest in the condensing diagram, which would be an argument in the direction of what is generally believed, viz., that the exhaust-passages for a condensing engine should be larger than for the same engine worked non-condensing. If the pressure in the condenser was quite steady at that noted, it is reasonably certain that the steam did not, under the same conditions, escape as readily into the condenser as into the atmosphere. But the regular decline of the line of counter-pressure of the condensing diagram, quite up to the point of exhaust-closure, points to the probability that the condenser—perhaps from being too small—did not "get hold" quite promptly, and that the pressure in it fluctuated considerably.

6

The condensing diagram shows that 25 per cent of the work is done below the atmosphere, and it is customary in such cases to credit the condenser with this amount. This is neither theoretically nor practically correct, because it assumes that if the engine was run non-condensing there would be no back-pressure, which is not so, and which, in such a calculation, would, so far as it goes, not give the condenser sufficient credit. It is also assumed that condensation in the cylinder would be the same whether the engine was run condensing or non-condensing, which also is not true, and which would tend to credit the condenser with more than its due. The compression is also different in the two instances, which further complicates the comparison. The only intelligible comparison that can be made is with the load in one instance equal to that in the other, as the pertinent question is how much the condenser will save in doing a definite amount of work. The steam accounted for by the indicator being in one instance 25 and in the other 16.7 pounds per horse-power per hour, the percentage in favor of the condenser is 33. The percentage of gain will not be so much as this, because of greater loss from condensation when the engine is condensing; it also costs something to operate the air-pump. It would not be safe to estimate the saving due to the use of the condenser at more than 25 per cent; but this conclusion is not reached because 25 per cent of the work happens to be done below the atmosphere. If the engine was to run non-condensing with this load, higher steam-pressure should be carried, which would increase the economy, making the difference still less. The economy of the engine running condensing would be better, theoretically, with steam of higher pressure, but perhaps not actually better.

Mention was made of the rounded corner in the admission-line. This is not especially, if in any degree, objectionable. It was only alluded to as showing that a little more lead might, for another purpose, be given. With the engine working non-condensing the cylinder is warmer and the rounded corner does not appear, indicating what is generally found to be true, viz., that a condensing engine requires more lead than one worked non-condensing.

COMPOUND CONDENSING-ENGINE DIAGRAMS.

The diagrams Figs. 18, 19, and 20 are from a pair of 18″ × 42″ automatic cut-off engines, compounded by adding an independent engine, with cylinder 40″ diameter, 42½″ stroke of piston. The high-pressure engines run at a speed of 83 and the low-pressure engine at 88 revolutions per minute. Figs. 18 and 19 are from the high-pressure cylinders, and Fig. 20 from the low-pressure cylinder.

The high-pressure diagrams show an initial pressure nearly equal to boiler-pressure (65 pounds), which owing to the piston-speed, falls off considerably before the point of cut-off is reached. In fact, the points of cut-off cannot be located with any degree of accuracy. The lead is unequal, and rather excessive, although it brings about a little higher initial pressure than would otherwise result, and probably does no particular harm if it results in smooth running. The points of exhaust opening and closure, also, are not alike. The time of

Fig. 18—Scale 40.

FIG. 19—SCALE 40.

exhaust-opening can be seen on the diagrams in Fig. 18, being indicated by a change from the direction of the expansion-lines, the pressure in the cylinder rising. instead of falling, as is usually the case when the exhaust-valve opens. This is due to the pressure in the steam-chest of the low-pressure cylinder being higher, at just this time, than the pressure of the expanded steam in the cylinder. The variation in pressure of the steam in the low-pressure steam-chest accounts for the unevenness of the lines of counter-pressure on the high-pressure diagrams. These diagrams, especially those in Fig. 19, show that the cut-off is not very well equalized. If steam had been worked alike in both ends of the cylinder, the expansion-curves would have crossed each other midway of the lengths of the diagrams—an end more nearly attained in Fig. 18 than in Fig. 19.

The diagrams from the low-pressure cylinder show very straight steam-lines, and a little inequality as to the amount of work done in the two ends of the cylinder, in the lead, and in the amount of the back-pressure. Of course, if thought desirable, the lead could be readily equalized as well as the cut-off, which is equally true of the high-pressure cylinders. The difference in back-pressure, between the two diagrams (Fig. 20), is more apparent on account of the low tension of the spring used in the indicator. It really amounts to less than $\frac{1}{2}$ pound.

In respect to hastily observing diagrams, it should be noted that in those taken with a spring of low tension, variations in the lines appear magnified to the eye, since diagrams are commonly taken with springs

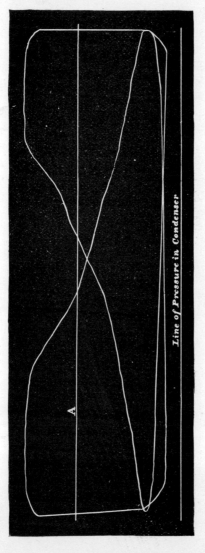

FIG. 20—SCALE 10.

of comparatively high tension, and the eye becomes educated to read them on this basis. In the instance of these diagrams a variation of one pound pressure is represented by $\frac{1}{10}$ of an inch, which is a very noticeable quantity.

The mean effective pressure (average of both cylinders) of the high-pressure diagrams is 23.8 pounds, and the horse-power 212.8. The mean effective pressure of the low-pressure diagrams is 8.62 pounds; horse-power, 204.5 ; total horse-power developed, 417.3. It is interesting to determine just how much the work done is increased by the addition of the low-pressure engine. If it is assumed that the average back-pressure of the high-pressure cylinders exhausting the quantity of steam used into the atmosphere would be one pound, the loss of mean effective pressure in these cylinders due to exhausting into the steam-chest of the low-pressure cylinder is 7 pounds, equivalent to 62.5 horse-power, the remainder—142 horse-power—being the work done by the low-pressure engine, without any cost in steam. This is not giving the low-pressure engine all the credit due it, because the higher pressure of steam in the high-pressure cylinders during the period of exhaust keeps them hotter, and reduces the inevitable loss from condensation.

It has been previously remarked that it is essential to know the pressure in the condenser, in order to determine how much back-pressure to charge against the cylinder. This is particularly important in this instance, since the condenser and air-pump were no part of the low-pressure engine, but were quite independent, located more than 50 feet away (measured

by the length of connecting-pipe), and some distance
higher than the cylinder. The exhaust from the
engine passes from the cylinder down to a heater
30 inches diameter and 16½ feet long, then up and
to the condenser. The vacuum-guage on the condenser showed a vacuum of 23 inches, or a pressure
of 3.4 pounds, as represented by the line on the
diagrams. Measuring from this, the back-pressure
which the engine is responsible for is only 2 pounds.
The heat extracted from the exhaust-steam in the
heater referred to was used for heating water to be
employed for various purposes in the mill, and it is to
be presumed that the loss from impaired vacuum was
more than made good by the heat saved in this way.

CHAPTER XII.

DIAGRAMS REPRESENTING VARIOUS PECULIARITIES.

IMPROPER ACTION OF CUT-OFF VALVE, AND RESTRICTED EXHAUST.

THE application of the indicator to the cylinder of a steam-engine not infrequently reveals curious conditions, and affords instructive texts against dispensing with the use of that instrument. The diagram in Fig. 21 was taken from a cylinder $18\frac{1}{2}''\times48''$, the engine running at 35 revolutions per minute; and the most interesting feature of the case is that it had been running ten years, all the time in condition to make just such a diagram. The cylinder had never been drilled for the indicator until the time when this diagram was taken, and then the indicator was applied to determine the horse-power used, the intention being to put in a new engine, not because this one did not work satisfactorily, but because it was believed to be overloaded, the estimate being that it was loaded to between 100 and 200 horse-power. The engine had originally a plain slide-valve, but had been changed to an automatic cut-off, the steam being cut off by a valve outside the steam-chest, the time of closing of which was under control of the governor. This kind of valve-motion is usually operated from the main valve

rock-arm or eccentric rod, the motion being the same
in direction as that of the main valve; but the lap

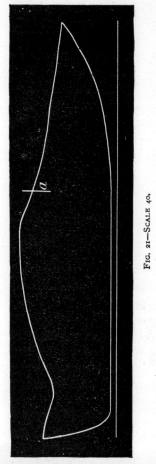

FIG. 21—SCALE 40.

being nothing, or less than that of the main slide, provides for its opening in advance of the latter.   In this

instance, however, it was operated by a separate eccen
tric, which was undoubtedly unfortunate, as if motion
had been communicated by the main rock-arm, it
would hardly have been possible to have arranged it so
badly.

The boiler-pressure was $60\frac{1}{2}$ pounds, out of which an
initial pressure of 30 pounds was realized, with a steam-
line that struggled along up to 42 pounds at half-stroke,
when the cut-off occurred. The point of cut-off is well
defined, showing a sharp closure of the cut-off valve.
This, with the compression and admission lines, are the
only tolerable features of the diagram. From the
point of cut-off the pressure falls only 18 pounds by
expansion, the volume of steam in the steam-chest
operating as clearance so far as expansion is concerned.
What this clearance amounts to, illustrated by length
added to the diagram, can be approximately determined.

Taking a point at a, directly after cut-off, the pressure from vacuum is 52 pounds, and at the end of the
stroke it is 39 pounds; that is, the pressure at the end
of the stroke is $\frac{39}{52} = \frac{3}{4}$ what it is at a. As the pressure varies inversely as the volume, the volume repre-
sented from a to the end of the stroke is one quarter
of the total volume represented from the clearance-line
to the end of stroke. The distance from a to the end
of the diagram is $1\frac{3}{4}$ inches; hence the whole volume
would be represented by a length of $1\frac{3}{4} \times 4 = 7$ inches,
that is, the clearance-line must be drawn 7 inches from
the end of the diagram, or about $2\frac{3}{4}$ inches from the
beginning. This enormous clearance (in the steam-
chest) has only to do with expansion, because before

the exhaust opens the communication between the steam-chest and cylinder is closed by the main valve. But it neutralizes the gain that would otherwise result from expansion.

The horse-power developed is 60, and the dry steam exhausted is 48½ pounds per horse-power per hour—at least twice what it ought to be. How much water was exhausted is not known, but there was so much in the cylinder that it was scarcely safe to keep the cylinder-cocks closed while taking a diagram. Alternate heating and cooling the large metallic surfaces inside the steam-chest doubtless contributed to increase the amount of water present in the cylinder ; this is always good argument against any cut-off arrangement in the use of which large surfaces of metal (other than those absolutely necessary) are subjected to alternate heating and cooling at every stroke.

Probably not less than 7 pounds of coal per horse-power per hour were used—say a ton a day more than should have been required. The engine had been running ten years in this condition, in which time it had wasted coal worth $15,000.

The cause of this is plainly shown by the diagram. Beginning with the compression-line, the pressure comes up very satisfactorily to 30 pounds, when the main valve opens the steam-port ; but instead of the pressure rising to within a pound or two of boiler-pressure, as the piston advances it falls to 26 pounds at about one eighth of the stroke. The reason of this is that the cut-off valve is behind, and has not opened for the admission of steam to the steam-chest, so that the only steam available for use in the cylinder for more than 6 inches of the stroke is that left in the steam-chest at the end of expansion in the other end of the cylinder and what leaked in past the poorly fitting cut-off valve. At about one eighth of the stroke, the cut-off valve, which should have opened early enough to have provided steam at full boiler-pressure in the steam-chest before the main valve uncovered the steam-port, begins to open slowly, and the pressure in the cylinder crawls up, so that the cut-off that should have taken place at less than one-quarter stroke takes place at one-half stroke. Then the volume of steam in the steam-chest, together with that in the cylinder, is expanded to about 40 pounds, absolute, instead of to 20 pounds, or less, as it would have been under favorable conditions. The exhaust opens late and the counter-pressure falls slowly, the back pressure being 5 pounds, when, at that speed, it should not have been more than one-half pound—a clear loss of more than 10 horse-power.

Altogether, it would be difficult to find worse conditions in an automatic engine, and it is safe to say that the application of the indicator ten years earlier would have pointed out a way to a very satisfactory saving. Such changes, for instance, as a steam-chest with the least practicable amount of unoccupied room, to reduce the clearance during expansion; a main valve with more steam lap and more travel, so that the exhaust would have opened earlier and more rapidly, thus reducing the back pressure, and the cut-off eccentric advanced so as to open the cut-off valve in advance of the main valve, would have been suggested by the first diagram taken. It is believed that the cut-off valve was adjusted for the late opening to make it possible to obtain a later cut-off than otherwise, under the impression that the capacity of the engine would be increased by this means. If so, the attempt was a first-class failure, as materially more work could have been done by setting the cut-off eccentric so as to get steam of very near boiler-pressure in the cylinder, and cutting off correspondingly early in the stroke.

PECULIARITIES OF EXPANSION-LINES—REOPENING OF
STEAM-VALVE.

Diagram 22 shows peculiarities in the expansion-line which are sometimes taken as representing improper action of the indicator. The real cause is worth investigation. It will be noticed that the expansion-line from a to b is substantially vertical in direction. This is only observed where the clearance is small. In such instances the pressure in the cylinder falls very rapidly directly after cut-off, because a small movement of the piston will serve to increase largely the *volume* of steam in the cylinder as compared with the volume at cut-off, and correspondingly decrease the pressure. In the cylinder from which this diagram was taken the clearance marked on the diagram is .0253 of the displacement of the piston, and the cut-off is about $\frac{1}{15}$ of the stroke. The steam being cut off with the suddenness of a blow at a, the piston travelling at a mean speed of between 500 and 600 feet per minute, and the distance horizontally from a to b representing less than one-inch motion of the piston, it will be seen that the pressure under the indicator-piston is almost *instantly* very ma-

terially reduced.   The spring being under considerable
tension starts the indicator-piston down, and the mo-

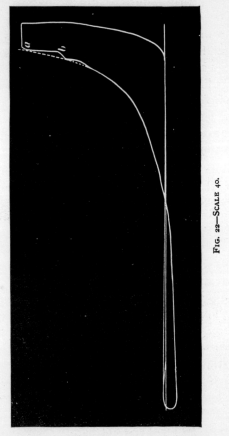

FIG. 22—SCALE 40.

mentum which it soon acquires carries the pencil ahead
of the position due to the steam-pressure, precisely as
in diagrams from high-speed engines, or in those taken

with a light spring, the pencil is found alternately too low and too high, the result being, a little later in the stroke, a regularly undulating line that is correctly taken as evidence of correct action of the indicator. In these instances the pencil will fall below its correct position, then the reaction will carry it above, and so on. In this instance the first evidence of reaction is at *b*, which is where the reciprocating parts of the indicator recover from the effects of their downward impetus. Had this occurred later the pencil would have been carried up considerably out of its true course, but at this early point in the stroke the pressure is falling too rapidly for this to occur, so that the reaction amounts to scarcely more than a pause in the downward motion. Below *b* a short distance there is another pause, after which the expansion-line gets into proper shape, being assisted by the more gradual fall in pressure as the volume of steam is increased. As previously noted, had precisely the same thing occurred later in the stroke, as from a cut-off when the volume of steam in the cylinder was twice or three times as great, the result would have been the wavy expansion-line frequently seen.

But there is still another cause that tends to produce a straight line from *a* to *b*. As has been previously explained, the actual curve of the diagram is usually found below the theoretical curve directly after cut-off, especially where full steam is worked for a small fraction of the stroke only, from the fact that condensation is taking place with great rapidity to supply the heat lost by the exposed surfaces during expansion and exhaust ; so that taking into considera-

7

tion both these causes, each operating in the same
direction, the position of the line from *a* to *b* is logi-
cally accounted for without attributing any fault to

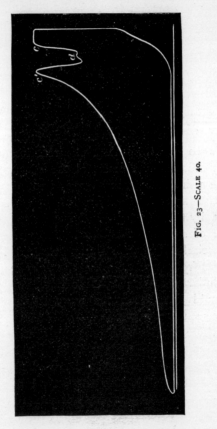

FIG. 23—SCALE 40.

the indicator, which, so far as can be seen from the diagram, was in good working condition. Finally, drawing the theoretical curve from the point of cut-off, the

variation is not nearly so great as a glance at the diagram would seem to indicate. A part of this curve is drawn in dotted line, and shows the variation a little greater than it actually is.

Diagram 23 shows peculiarities that cannot be explained in this way. The initial pressure was 60 pounds—one pound less than boiler-pressure—and the valve closed very sharply at *c*, after the piston had made a small fraction—about 5 per cent—of its stroke. The effort to recover after the usual somewhat too rapid fall of the pencil is seen at *d*, and from some cause the pressure rises again to nearly 60 pounds, making, apparently, two points, *c*, *c'*, of cut-off. The cause of this was that the cut-off valve, which dropped in closing, afterward left its seat, and from the amplitude of the steam-ports actually admitted steam of nearly boiler-pressure the second time. From a short distance below *c'* the line falls too slowly for some distance, showing that the valve leaked while settling back against its seat. The engine from which this diagram was taken was a small one, and the aggregate length of the ports controlled by the cut-off valve was equal to about twice the diameter of the cylinder. With this length of port the cut-off proper occurred while the valve was dropping at its highest velocity, and through only a very short distance. The effect of this was that the pressure in the cylinder was not reduced enough while the valve was closing so that the unbalanced pressure in the steam-chest would hold the valve to its seat against the jar of the air-cushion which stopped it.

There were two remedies that suggested themselves, one of which was to provide for closing the valve slower, and the other to arrange a guard to pre-

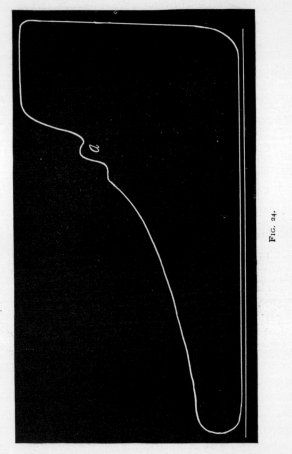

FIG. 24.

vent the valve leaving the seat, horizontally. The last remedy was the one tried, with success.

Trouble similar to this, though not so marked in extent, often occurs in four-valve engines. The result generally appears somewhat later in the stroke in the form of an irregularity in the expansion-line, as at *a*, Fig. 24, followed by an expansion-line much too high, and high terminal pressure. This is usually explained as being the result of wet steam, a small cylinder, or in any but the correct way. The true explanation is that the valve does not close properly, or reopens a little, and does not get properly seated until some distance beyond where cut-off *apparently* takes place. It is needless saying that this diagram represents an important waste of steam.

ECCENTRIC OUT OF PLACE.

Diagram 25 was referred to the writer for explanation on the supposition that the admission-line was at the left, and that cut-off was at *e*, the query being, Why the expansion-line got down so low at *b*? It was known that the eccentric was out of position when the diagram was taken. A little reflection showed that it was a mistake to suppose the left to be the admission end of the diagram, and starting wrong efforts to read it were of course fruitless. Why this conclusion was arrived at is the special feature of interest, as it will generally aid in unravelling " crooked " diagrams. The reasoning was as follows : If the admission was at the left, then *dc* is the admission-line and *cb* the expansion-curve. But *dc* is an impossible admission-line (for late admission) because it curves downwards, and *cd* is an impossible expansion-line because it curves upwards.

It would, perhaps, be possible by bringing about

peculiar leaks to get either of these lines, but it is entirely improbable that leaks occurring in the ordinary way should be responsible for changing the direction

FIG. 25—SCALE 40.

of flexure of either as shown. When it comes to so changing both lines, the possibility of it is not worth consideration.

Beginning at the other end of the diagram,—at the right,—the reading of it is plain enough: At *a* the piston begins to move ahead, but the valve being behind time the admission-port is covered. There is at this time a pressure of 26 pounds absolute in the clearance-space. The piston moving along and the port remaining covered, the pressure falls by expansion to *b*. At this point—about one-quarter stroke— the valve begins to open the port, but the motion of the piston is so rapid and the space to be filled with steam so large that the pressure increases slowly, as represented by the line *bc*; it is in respect to this line an aggravated case of late admission without assistance from compression. Under these conditions the upward flexure of the line *bc* is accounted for; it is exactly what would be expected.

At *c* steam is cut off; *cd* is the expansion-line, concave downward and inward as it should be. The exhaust opens late at *d*, for which reason the pressure falls slowly, till beyond *e* it is equal to that against which the piston is working. The line from *d*, by *e*, to *a* is the line of counter-pressure, there being no compression.

The engine from which this diagram was taken is 22″ × 30″, running at 75 revolutions. The engine kept running, doing its regular work with the misplaced eccentric, but pounded so badly the indicator was applied to ascertain the cause. The exhaust was against the high pressure shown, because the exhaust-steam at that pressure was used for other purposes requiring that pressure. But for this use of the exhaust-steam the trouble would have manifested itself at the coal-pile.

CHAPTER XIII.

INITIAL EXPANSION—SMALL STEAM-PIPE.

ECONOMY OF INITIAL EXPANSION.

THE greatest economy in the use of steam in the steam-engine being, broadly speaking, when the terminal pressure is lowest compared with the mean effective pressure, it follows that a fall of pressure in the cylinder previous to cut-off, usually called initial expansion, represents a loss when occurring in an automatic cut-off engine, because it makes the cut-off occur later than it otherwise would, increasing to a corresponding extent the terminal pressure. Hence, in this type of engine the effort is made to provide for a steam-line as straight and as near boiler-pressure as practicable without sacrificing too much in some other direction to obtain it. There is undoubtedly a point in all ordinarily constructed engines beyond which it is the reverse of economical to go in this direction—a point somewhere short of boiler-pressure in the cylinder, and short of an absolutely straight steam-line. Just how far it represents economy in the use of steam to go in the direction of a perfect steam-line depends upon a variety of circumstances. Small valves do not consume so much of the power of the engine in their operation as larger ones (of the same kind), and as there is inevitably some leakage, it is

naturally greater where the ports are long than where
they are short; it is also understood that a balanced
valve moves easier than an unbalanced one—all of
which is entitled to consideration in determining what
the character of the steam-line should be.

But while it is true that initial expansion, to any
great extent, usually represents a loss of economy in

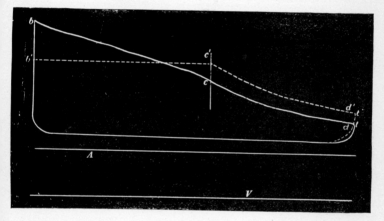

FIG. 26—SCALE 30.

the instance of an engine in which the governor operates to vary the point of cut-off, it is equally true that
when the cut-off is fixed and the speed controlled by
means of a throttling governor, initial expansion usually represents gain, sometimes in a marked degree.
This is because it then has the effect of bringing about
lower terminal pressure for a given mean effective
pressure.

While initial expansion is, perhaps, properly enough

called throttling, the distinction should be sharply made between throttling that results only in reducing the initial pressure, and that which provides for a gradual fall in the pressure from that nearly equal to boiler-pressure to a point materially lower at cut-off.

The diagram, Fig. 26 (in full lines), shows a fair amount of initial expansion, and will illustrate the gain brought about by it, which may be more or less, according to circumstances. It is from a 12″ × 20″ engine, running at 90 revolutions, valve adjusted to cut off at 11″, or at *c* on the diagram. The boiler-pressure was 50 pounds, 39 pounds of which was realized in the cylinder at the beginning of the stroke, the pressure falling from that pressure at *b*, to 22 pounds at *c*, by initial expansion, and then by regular expansion to a terminal pressure, *t*, of 24 pounds absolute. The gain by initial expansion may be determined by comparing the actual diagram with the one plotted in dotted lines, both diagrams representing equal work. In the latter the pressure remains constant from *b′* to *c′*, the initial pressure being 27 pounds, or that required with the straight steam-line to make the mean effective pressure equal that of the actual diagram. Since the mean effective pressures of the two diagrams are the same, we can approximate the saving from initial expansion by calculations from the weight of steam at pressures *t* and *t′*. The pressure (absolute) at *t* is 24 pounds, and the weight per cubic foot at that pressure .0610 pound. At *t′* the pressure is 27 pounds, weight of a cubic foot .0683 pound; difference, .0073 pound, or about 11 per cent. If the saving from exhaust-closure were accounted for, this percentage would be increased; but 11 per cent is a safe estimate in this case, letting the saving from exhaust-closure offset a little more condensation as the result of admitting steam of higher pressure.

The steam-lines of diagrams from engines in which the speed is controlled by throttling will be of a variety of forms, according to existing conditions and the construction of the engine. There is quite as much difference in the economy of such engines, whether fitted with separate expansion-valves or not, as there is between different automatic cut-off engines, and it is just as readily determined by the use of the indicator, notwithstanding which the indicator is seldom applied to this class of steam-engines. Its intelligent use, changing the construction in accordance with what was learned from its indications, would result in as much gain in efficiency, comparatively, as has been the case in the instance of the automatic cut-off engine.

DIAGRAMS FROM THE SAME ENGINE WITH SMALL AND LARGE STEAM-PIPES.

The effect of using a small steam pipe, for an automatic engine, by which initial pressure is reduced and expansion shortened, resulting in high terminal pressure, may be seen by a comparison of diagrams 27 and 28. They were taken from an automatic engine $12'' \times 30''$, at a speed of 95 revolutions per minute. When 27 was taken, steam was supplied through 30 feet of $2\frac{1}{2}$-inch pipe, with three elbows in its length. Diagram 28 was taken after a four-inch pipe had been substituted.

Diagram 27 shows, as compared with 28, a loss equal to 12½ per cent in steam used, and it also shows

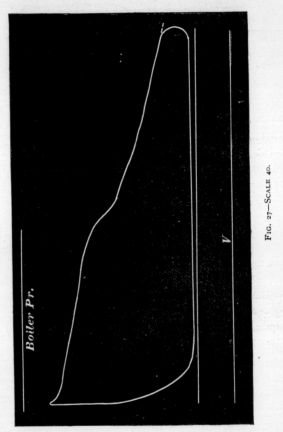

Fig. 27—Scale 40.

that in an emergency but little more work could be got from the engine; a small increase of work, or reduction in steam-pressure, and the engine would not run up to speed. Even when running under the conditions shown, in changes of load, such as throwing

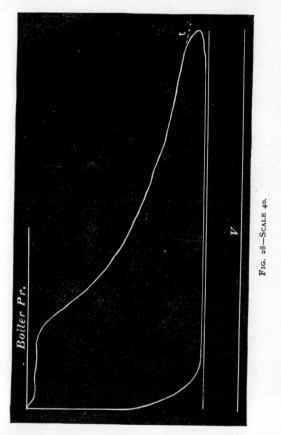

Fig. 28—Scale 40.

on machinery that had been thrown off, it would be found that the governor had but little control over the motion; in other words, that the engine would be very slow in getting up to speed. The loss in this respect might, in some kinds of work, be more serious than the loss of steam.

With the large steam-pipe in use when 28 was taken there is a fair margin for governing, either when the steam-pressure is reduced, or the load increased, because with the higher initial pressure the required mean effective pressure is had with a cut-off at one-quarter stroke, while if necessary steam may be admitted till a little later than half-stroke. With the large steam-pipe the high mean effective and low terminal pressure necessary to economy is had.

It is always best in any engine to have the steam-pipe of ample size; then, if it is desirable to bring about a reduction of initial pressure, do it by throttling.

CHAPTER XIV.

DETECTING LEAKY VALVES — LIGHT FLY-WHEEL.

LEAKY STEAM AND EXHAUST VALVES.

DIAGRAMS Fig. 29 are from a four-valve engine 20″ × 60″, running at 57 revolutions; boiler-pressure about 70 pounds. They are not good ones. The cut-off is not as prompt as it usually is in this class of engines, and the exhaust opens too late. This late exhaust-opening results in a material loss from back-pressure at and near the beginning of the return stroke in *B*, and substantially the same loss would undoubtedly be shown in *A* if the terminal pressure were not so much lower.

Another fault is that the work done is not equalized between the two ends. This equalization should be brought about, and the exhaust-valves opened at least two inches earlier in the stroke.

But the diagrams show evidence of a graver fault than either of these, viz., leaky valves. While the indicator cannot always be relied upon to detect leaky valves and piston if the leak is small, when it is large it will do so in almost every instance if diagrams are taken from both ends of the cylinder. Leakage of steam into or out of the cylinder will influence the character of the expansion-curve. If steam leaks out of the cylinder the terminal pressure will be lower than

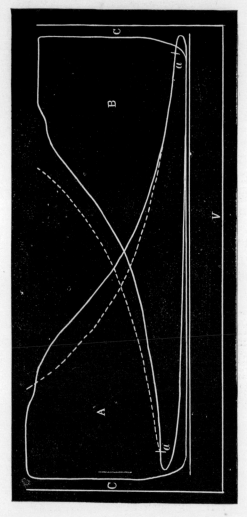

FIG. 29—SCALE 40.

it otherwise would be; if it leaks into the cylinder it will be higher. If both steam and exhaust valves leak, the leaks might possibly balance each other, but there is no probability that this would be the case in each end of the cylinder.

At a piston-speed of 400 to 600 feet per minute, the terminal pressure should not, in cylinders of 12 inches and upward in diameter, be more than 2 pounds above the termination of the theoretical curve. If found higher than this, there is a probability of leaky steam-valves. If the theoretical curve ends lower than the actual curve, the presumption is that the exhaust-valves or the piston leaks.

In Fig. 14, the theoretical curve, drawn from a point just after cut-off, showed a terminal pressure so high as to lead to the belief that steam leaked into the cylinder. In the instance of Fig. 29, it is difficult to tell, even approximately, where cut-off occurred, so a different plan is pursued; that is, the curves are drawn from a point *a* just before exhaust-opening. They show just as clearly that in *B* there is a good deal more steam present at the termination of the stroke than at cut-off, wherever it may have been, and that in *A* there was about as much less. There is every reason to conclude that in one instance steam leaks freely into the cylinder, and that in the other it leaks out about as freely. All the valves, steam and exhaust, probably leak, but on one end the steam-valve leaks most, while the same is true of the exhaust-valve on the other end. If both diagrams were like *A*, the leak *might* all be by the piston. If both were like *B*, it would be possible, but highly improbable, at this pis-

8

ton-speed that re-evaporation in the cylinder was the cause of the increased quantity of steam present. There would not be time at a piston-speed of nearly 600 feet to condense sufficient water to increase the quantity of steam to such an extent, or time to re-evaporate it if it entered the cylinder as water.

It may be remarked, that when a little too much steam is found in the cylinder at the end of the stroke, as indicated by the expansion curve drawn from near exhaust-opening keeping just sensibly above the real curve, or the curve drawn from near cut-off falling a pound or two below it near the end of the stroke, it is accounted for, usually, by re-evaporation in the cylinder. But when too small an amount of steam is found it is evidence of leak; this refers to the use of ordinary steam, that is, steam that is not superheated.

There is evidence enough in either of these diagrams, considered singly, to lead to a belief that the valves were leaky; taken together, the evidence is conclusive.

When we have a pair of diagrams like these it is generally possible to detect leaky valves without knowing the clearance, which is necessary for drawing the correct theoretical curves. Thus in this instance the clearance might be assumed to be anything, say 6 per cent. Upon this assumption, if the theoretical curves were drawn they would still show that in one diagram there was too much steam at exhaust-opening, and in the other not so much as there should be. When leaks exist to the extent here indicated, there is a very serious loss of steam.

A LIGHT FLY-WHEEL.

The diagrams in Fig. 30 illustrate an aggravated case of attempting to bring about good regulation in a throttling-engine provided with a fly-wheel too light for the purpose. The fly-wheel has an important bearing on the fuel economy of any engine, either throt-

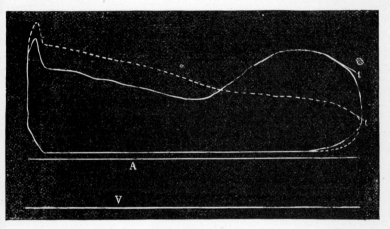

Fig. 30—Scale 40.

tling or automatic cut-off, but unfortunately in the throttling-engine this receives but little consideration.

The steam-line of this diagram (in full lines) has, at the beginning, the proper direction for producing a good throttling diagram—that is, good for the amount of work being done;—but somewhat later than half-stroke, the governor-valve opens suddenly, apparently its full capacity, admitting steam till near the end of the stroke the pressure exceeds the initial pressure by six pounds, and this at a time when the steam thus admitted can do but little work before it is exhausted. This admission of steam late in the stroke, so that the terminal pressure measured from atmosphere is, in some instances, equal to or higher than the mean effective pressure, is the loss likely to result from the attempt to use a light fly-wheel and a good governor. Years ago, when governors were in use that began to act some seconds after a variation in speed, the wasteful effects of a light fly-wheel were not so noticeable, because it was as good as the governor, which had not sufficient energy to waste much steam. But with the modern high-speeded regulator, that almost anticipates change of speed, good steam-economy cannot be expected without proper dimensions of fly-wheel.

The engine from which this diagram was taken was bought second-hand, but was in good condition and had well-designed, ample ports. It had, also, a fairly-proportioned fly-wheel pulley, but it being inconvenient to belt from this fly-wheel, and a fly-wheel being nothing more than a pulley to the parties who bought and put the engine up, a pulley of less diameter and less than one quarter the weight was substituted.

Starting at the beginning of the stroke, and assuming the diagram from the other end of the cylinder to have been a duplicate of this (which it was very nearly), the action of the governor and influence of lack of fly-wheel can be studied. Thus the speed may be assumed to be normal at the beginning, and the governor-valve in about the right position, but the steam-chest pressure is too low. With the light wheel and the low steam-chest pressure, the speed falls off, so that at about mid-stroke the governor is induced to act, which it does by fully opening the valve; then, there being but little resistance in the wheel, the speed is acceler- ated sufficiently to quite close the governor-valve at about the time the lap of the slide-valve operates to cut off steam. It seems probable that the governor- valve remained closed until about the time steam was admitted for the return stroke, or a little later, the steam required to fill the clearance-space accounting for the initial pressure being less than the pressure in the steam-chest at the time of cut-off. To make this diagram would require about 75 pounds of water per horse-power per hour, and the boiler required such hard firing to evaporate the quantity of water nec- essary, that more than 12 pounds of coal per horse- power were burned; in fact, but for the difficulty in keeping steam, the engine might still have been run- ning as it was when this diagram was taken, as the governor kept the speed *in revolutions per minute* very regular, and the indicator was applied to the engine *because the boiler was too small.*

To remedy matters, and keep the small pulley to belt from, a fly-wheel with a narrow and deep rim was put on beside the pulley, and without further change the diagram shown in dotted lines was taken. This is .a very good throttling diagram, with the exception that the cylinder is too large for the work, which brings about low initial pressure. The water required when this diagram was taken would be about 50 in place of 75 pounds—a saving of 33 per cent. The saving in coal was more than this, as decreased con- sumption brought about more economical use.

The only other faults of the diagrams are too little compression to insure smooth running, and—if it is a fault—a slight lack of lead.

To insure proper action in a governor, the fly-wheel must be of sufficient weight to allow the crank to pass the centres where steam has no effect in moving the piston, without sensible decrease in the speed ; also, to allow diminution of pressure during the stroke by initial expansion without a reduction of speed sufficient to induce over-action of the governor.   A few pounds of metal in the fly-wheel often results in a large saving of steam.

CHAPTER XV.

DIAGRAMS FROM LOCOMOTIVE-ENGINES.

HOW TO CONNECT THE INDICATOR.

BUT little attention, comparatively, has been given to indicating locomotive-engines. At first thought it may seem somewhat difficult to get diagrams from a locomotive swinging along at 60 miles an hour, but if suitable preparations are made there is nothing worth the name of difficulty in doing it. It will be found advisable to pipe the two ends of the cylinder together, using one indicator. The holes should be drilled in the outer side of cylinder, at the centre, up and down, for $\frac{3}{4}$-inch pipe, the pipe connecting to a three-way cock at the centre, in which the indicator-cock is screwed; the pipe should be kept as close to the cylinder as practicable. Thus arranged, the indicator will stand at the centre of the cylinder lengthwise, and near the bottom of the steam-chest.

DRUM-MOTION.

The drum-motion may be had by using the arrangement of lever shown in Fig. 31, which is essentially the same as that shown in Fig. 1. The reducing-lever and connection should be made of steel, with thimbles made fast in the ends so as to provide bearings not less than $\frac{1}{2}$ inch in diameter, and about $1\frac{1}{2}$ inches in

FIG. 31.

length. The upper end of the lever swings on a pin made fast in an angle-iron bolted to the running-board, and the outer end of the connection journals on a stud screwed in the cross-head: this stud must be long enough to carry the lever so far out that the cord will

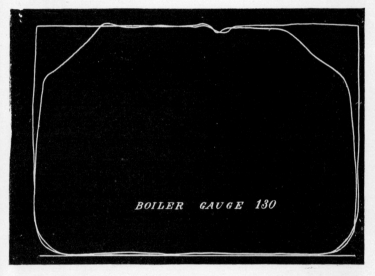

BOILER GAUGE 130

Fig. 32—Scale 50.

4 miles per hour.   Reverse-lever in 7th notch.   Throttle open.   Grade 47½ feet per mile.

lead direct to the indicator in a straight line fore and aft.

Any other suitable arrangement with which no guide-pulleys are employed may be used instead of this, but the one shown will generally be found a convenient one.

SAFETY PRECAUTIONS.

A place must be boxed up, the box being securely bolted to the bumper and cylinder, or other parts, in which to sit while taking the diagrams. The outside and front of this box should be so high as to prevent

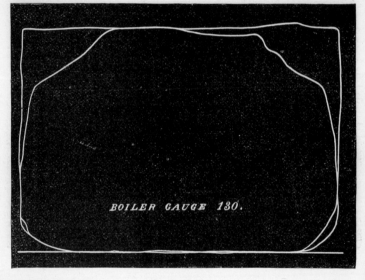

Fig. 33—Scale 50.

8.30 miles per hour. Reverse-lever in 5th notch. Throttle open. Grade 36 feet per mile.

the possibility of the operator being thrown out by a lurch of the engine; both hands are fully employed in handling the indicator, and the attention is concentrated on the operation, so no thought about safety should be necessary. With these precautions diagrams

may be taken about as comfortably from a locomotive
as from a stationary engine at the same speed.

HOW TO PRESERVE THE DATA.

The operator *can* note the necessary data on the diagrams as he takes them, but it is inconvenient for him to

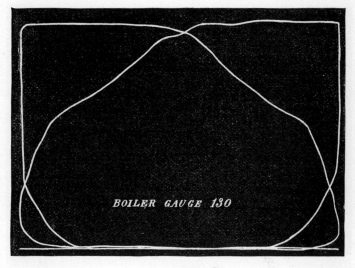

BOILER GAUGE 130

Fig. 34—Scale 50.

11.06 miles per hour.   Reverse-lever in 4th notch.   Throttle two thirds open.
Grade 47½ feet per mile.

do so. It is better that he have an assistant, and arrange
as follows: Number as many blanks as will be required,
from one upward, and arrange them in a package convenient to be come at in the order of the numbers.
The assistant takes his place in the cab, provided with
a book in which are written numbers corresponding to

those on the indicator-blanks. The operator begins with No. 1 blank, and when the assistant observes him remove it from the drum, he enters against 1 in his book the steam-pressure, positions of throttle and reverse levers, speed and location on the road. This is repeated with No. 2, and so on. Some of the dia-

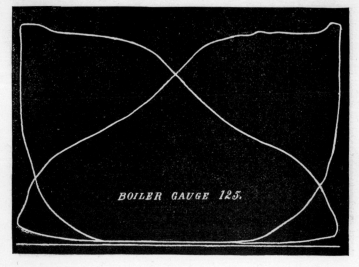

Fig. 35—Scale 50.

15.49 miles per hour.   Reverse-lever in 3d notch.   Throttle open.   Grade 42 feet per mile.

grams may be worthless, but the entries will have been made the same, and if the assistant watches the operator his entries will tally correctly with the numbers on the diagram.

Exactly the same reasoning that applies to diagrams from other engines applies to those from locomotives.

From the character of the valve-motion compression will be high at short cut-off, and back-pressure at high speed will be what in stationary-engine practice would be considered excessive. Owing to high compression, clearance cannot be satisfactorily reduced so low as it

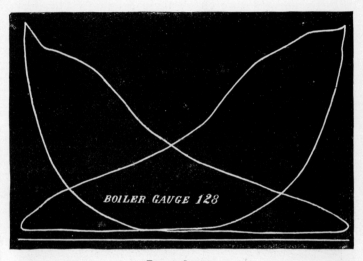

BOILER GAUGE 128

FIG. 36—SCALE 50.

34.31 miles per hour. Reverse-lever in 2d notch. Throttle open. Grade 42 feet per mile.

otherwise could be. Compression should never exceed steam-chest pressure at the shortest cut-off.

DIAGRAMS REPRESENTING GOOD PRACTICE.

The diagrams 32 to 37, inclusive, represent good American practice in the way of steam-distribution in locomotive-cylinders. They were taken from a locomotive running on freight-service. The cylinders are

18″×24″, steam-ports 1¼″×16″, full travel of valve 5 inches, outside lap of valve ⅞ inch, inside lap ⅛ inch, lead at full stroke 1/10 inch. The driving-wheels (outside of tires) are 62 inches diameter. The weight of train, including tender, was 1,301,700 pounds.

The back-pressure on all these diagrams is low for

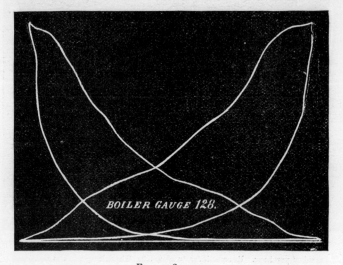

FIG. 37—SCALE 50.

14.75 miles per hour.   Reverse-lever in 1st notch.   Throttle open.   Grade 30 feet per mile.

locomotive practice, and the mean effective pressure for the different grades of expansion is high ; Fig. 32 is noticeable for showing remarkably high mean effective pressure. The work done in the two ends of the cylinder is very nearly equal. As representing good valve-setting, these diagrams may serve as models; they are seldom equalled in this respect.

It will be observed at short cut-off that the initial pressure is not nearly so well maintained up to cut-off as in stationary engines; but in cylinders so much ex-

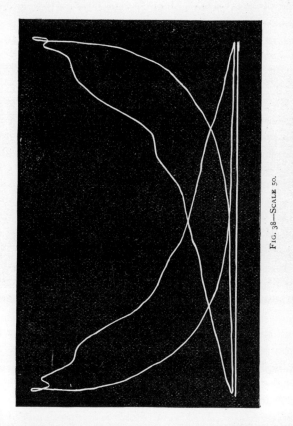

FIG. 38—SCALE 50.

posed as locomotive-cylinders are, some wire-drawing, which results in slight superheating, is not objection-able. The cylinders, for obvious reasons, are large for the work at high speeds, and some reduction in initial pressure and high compression avoids what would otherwise be too low terminal pressure. By increasing compression more steam is saved by earlier exhaust-closure; hence the saving in this way balances the apparent loss from high terminal pressure due to increased compression.

TOO MUCH COMPRESSION.

Fig. 38 represents a pair of diagrams from a passenger-locomotive working at short cut-off. Compression is carried too far. In such a case loss is likely to occur from a springing up of the edge of the valve, permitting steam to blow through into the exhaust. The tendency is also to wear the valve in such shape that it will leak. If so short cut-off is to be employed, there should be more clearance. With a little later cut-off exhaust-closure would be delayed, and then the clearance would be sufficient.

It cannot be known except by trial with the indicator what the effect of a given clearance will be so far as concerns compression. Compression will seldom be as high as would appear from calculation owing to heat being rapidly taken up to warm the exposed surfaces of the cylinder. At high-speed compression will be higher than at low-speed, because there is less time for the transfer of heat, and because back-pressure is generally higher at high-speed.

MODERATE AND HIGH SPEED COMPARED.

Diagrams 39 and 40 were taken from a locomotive with cylinders $16'' \times 24''$, steam-ports $1\frac{1}{4}'' \times 14''$, full travel of valve $4\frac{1}{2}$ inches, outside lap $\frac{3}{4}$ inch, lead $\frac{1}{16}$ inch to $\frac{1}{4}$ inch. The driving-wheels were 60 inches diameter. Fig. 39 was taken at a speed of 35 miles

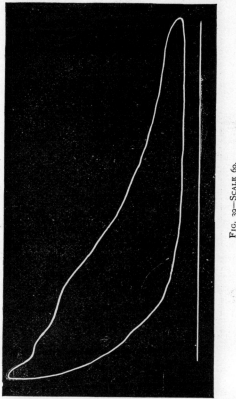

FIG. 39—SCALE 60.

per hour, the engine hauling a light train; 40 was taken at a speed of 60 miles per hour, engine running light. The two speeds correspond to piston-speeds of

9

784 and 1344 feet per minute, respectively; boiler pressure in both instances 125 pounds.

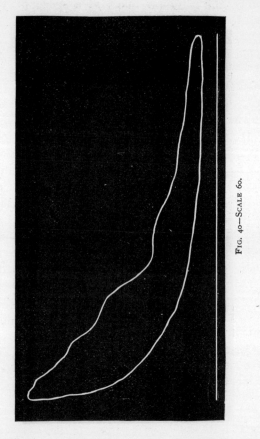

FIG. 40—SCALE 60.

The effect of the higher speed is plainly seen in the reduced area of 40; but with ports so small for such piston-speed the reduction of area is less than would be expected. If it were not for compression there would undoubtedly be much greater difference between the diagrams. Compression in 40 is accountable for the close approximation to boiler-pressure, and this high pressure at the beginning helps in keeping the pressure up to the end of the stroke. Both diagrams show a good deal of falling off in pressure—initial expansion—before cut-off, and this is of course the greatest at the higher speed—that is, in 40. The back-pressure is also somewhat higher in 40. In both 39 and 40 the back-pressure increases as the opening for exhaust gradually narrows, so much so that it cannot be told from either diagram where exhaust-closure took place. This increase in back-pressure before exhaust-closure is greater in 40 than in 39, owing to the higher speed.

In calculating loss from back-pressure it should be reckoned up to the point of exhaust-closure only; after that the steam present is saved for further use. But as increase of pressure at the time of exhaust-closure increases the pressure at the end of compression, and as at this point it should not be greater than steam-chest pressure, it follows that if there were never more than 3 or 4 instead of 10 or 15 pounds pressure (above atmosphere) when the exhaust closed, clearance might be less.

ECONOMY OF THE LINK-MOTION.

The diagram in full lines, Fig. 41, is from a locomotive-engine with cylinders $16'' \times 22''$, at a speed of 248 revolutions, or a piston-speed of 909 feet, per minute. This diagram is interesting as compared with those

taken with other forms of cut-off, since it is quite generally held to be a fact that the link is very inefficient

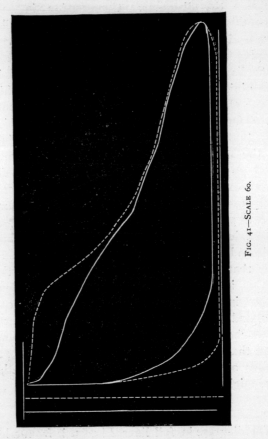

FIG. 41—SCALE 60.

as a means of working steam expansively, the loss as
compared with other means of steam - distribution
being variously estimated at from 25 to 40 per cent.

In order more clearly to make this comparison, a hypothetical diagram has been plotted in dotted lines, which, I believe, will be accounted a very good one indeed for an automatic cut-off engine at that piston-speed.

The important points of loss in the distribution of steam by the link-motion are claimed to be: A failure to approximate boiler-pressure in the cylinder; too early release; excessive back-pressure; too early exhaust-closure, and excessive clearance, the last in part being necessary to avoid too high compression incident to early exhaust-closure. When this diagram was taken the boiler-pressure was 128 pounds, and the cut-off at $8\frac{1}{2}$ inches. The initial pressure is about 14 pounds less than boiler-pressure.

Of this it may here be remarked, that the highest point reached by the pencil does not at high speed and sharp lead, represent initial pressure in the cylinder, but rather the inertia of the reciprocating parts of the indicator, which always under such circumstances carries the pencil higher than is due to the steam pressure in the cylinder.

Besides the lack of boiler-pressure in the cylinder there is a fall of pressure (initial expansion) of 19 pounds before cut-off. This lack of pressure at the beginning of the stroke and fall of pressure before cut-off represent loss to some extent, although, as previously said, all is not loss that appears to be. There is no evidence of material loss from too early release, and there is none too much compression for the amount of clearance-space. The line of counter-pressure shows the back-pressure to be about 6 pounds. The loss from this is apparent, but is modified by early exhaust-closure. Some saving would result from reducing the clearance and compression—that is, if both were reduced.

Comparing the actual with the hypothetical diagram, the efficiency of the latter over the former is between 14 and 15 per cent, not 25 or 40 per cent. That is, assuming that the clearance, $7\frac{1}{2}$ per cent, as represented by the full clearance-line, could with safety be reduced one half, as represented by the dotted clearance-line; that the back-pressure may be less than 2 pounds, and that as good steam-line as that shown in the dotted diagram may be had, the dry steam exhausted would be 20 pounds per hour for the actual, and a little more than 17 for the hypothetical, diagram. This would not be all gain, as the somewhat greater extremes of temperature in the cylinder in the instance of the hypothetical diagram would result in correspondingly greater condensation, and hence loss.

It is customary with those who condemn the link-motion to stop here and charge all this loss of efficiency to it. As a matter of fact, the link is responsible for only a very small part of it. To appreciate this it is only necessary to look at another condition that equally with the valve-motion influences the steam-distribution, viz., the dimensions of ports. In this case the steam-ports are $1\frac{1}{4}'' \times 14''$, in area between $\frac{1}{11}$th and $\frac{1}{12}$th that of the piston. In the best stationary-engine practice, with which it is the custom to compare the link-motion, this proportion would not be accepted for a piston-speed much greater than one half that at which this diagram was taken; and to produce a diagram equal to the one sketched for comparison from a modern automatic cut-off stationary engine, the area of ports would need to be nearly double what it is in this case. If the area of the ports is increased as indicated, and the link-motion used, the most of this difference against it will disappear. The opinion that small ports are a part of the link-motion, or at least that they are a necessity when the link is used, although entirely without foundation, is almost universal. By balancing or relieving the valve of pressure, as is done in stationary-engine practice, there is no more objection to large ports in one instance than in the other.

With regard to the 6 pounds back-pressure, the outside lap of valve is $\frac{3}{4}$ inch, inside lap o; hence the area of port-opening for exhaust at the beginning of the return-stroke is not less than 11 square inches, *while all the steam exhausted must pass through a nozzle having an area of only 5 square inches,* something not always considered in discussing the efficiency of the link-motion.

The diagram shows, so far as a diagram from the link-motion at a single point of cut-off and from one end of the cylinder can show, very correct valve-setting. Compression cannot well be carried higher, because it is necessary to provide for shorter cut-off, in which the exhaust-closure will be earlier.

STEAM-CONSUMPTION MEASURED FROM A LOCOMOTIVE-
DIAGRAM.

Fig. 42 illustrates the calculation of the steam-consumption from a locomotive - diagram according to Thompson's table. Measuring the mean effective pressure it is found to be 36.25 pounds, and the ter-minal pressure above vacuum is 31.2. In the table against 31 and under 2 is the number 1062.859. This number divided by 36.25 gives 29.3, the steam-consumption uncorrected for clearance and compression.

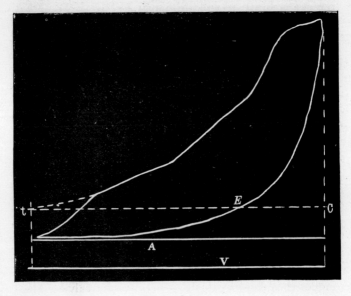

Fig. 42—Scale 50.

The length of line *tE* is 2.3 inches, and of *tC* 3.2 inches; hence

$$\frac{29.3 \times 2.3}{3.2} = 21,$$

the pounds of dry steam exhausted per horse-power per hour. Assuming the water present to have been 20 per cent of the steam, the water-consumption per horse-power per hour would be about 25¼ pounds. This diagram is not used because it is a particularly good one so far as economy is concerned, but because it happens to be a good one for the purpose for which it is wanted.

FINDING THE HORSE-POWER.

In computing the horse-power from locomotive-diagrams it is convenient to find a constant multiplier for one pound mean effective pressure and one revolution per minute; then the mean effective pressure multiplied by the revolutions per minute and by this constant multiplier will give the horse-power of any diagram. Thus, say the area of piston is 250 inches, and the stroke 24 inches: each revolution gives 4 feet piston-travel, and a constant multiplier for ore cylinder of that engine is

$$\frac{250 \times 1 \times 4}{33000} = .0303.$$

Suppose the revolutions per minute when a particular diagram was taken to have been 200, and the mean effective pressure of the diagram 60 pounds, then $200 \times 60 \times .0303 = 363.6$, the horse-power of one cylinder.

THE EFFECT ON THE DIAGRAM OF THE STEAM-DISTRIBUTION PECULIAR TO THE LOCOMOTIVE.

An inspection of any of the diagrams from locomotives taken at short cut-off illustrates why it is comparatively easy to get such diagrams at high speeds. At high speed cut-off is short, and compression begins early in the return-stroke, previous to which the back-pressure is somewhat increased by the gradual narrowing up of the port-opening. The pencil and other reciprocating parts of the indicator are thus gradually started upward, and occupy considerable *time* in getting to their highest position. At the same speed in an engine in which exhaust-closure does not occur until near the end of the return-stroke the pencil is forced more nearly instantly to its highest position, and the inertia of the reciprocating parts of the indicator plays an important part in distorting the diagram.

Cut-off in the locomotive at high speed is also gradual, and the decrease of pressure previous to cut-off is considerable, so the fall of the pencil is gradual rather than abrupt. If the attempt were made to get a diagram from an engine in which the steam-distribution was like that represented in Figs. 10 or 22, at a speed corresponding to 60 miles an hour with the locomotive, considerable trouble would be experienced.

CHAPTER XVI.

OTHER USES OF THE INDICATOR.

STEAM-CHEST DIAGRAMS.

THUS far the indicator has been considered in its application to the cylinder of the steam-engine. It is equally applicable to the cylinders of air and gas engines, or to any purpose where quickly varying fluid-pressure is to be recorded. In connection with the steam-engine its application to the steam-pipe or steam-chest is frequently important. If upon applying the indicator to the cylinder of a steam-engine it is found that there is a material loss of pressure between the boiler and cylinder, it is desirable to know what is responsible for this loss. The stricture may be in the ports, or it may be in the steam-pipe. If the indicator is applied to the steam-chest, motion being had the same as when it is used on the cylinder, it will show what the pressure is there during the stroke of the piston, and by comparison how much of the loss of pressure is due to the effort of the steam in getting through the ports.

A diagram something like 43 may be expected from the steam-chest. This diagram was taken from the steam-chest of an automatic engine with boiler-pressure 75 pounds, represented by *B*. When the valve

opens for admission the pressure suddenly falls to *C,*
about 2 pounds. Steam is cut off at *D,* from which
point the pressure rises very quickly to *E,* 2 pounds
higher than boiler-pressure. It seemed at first that

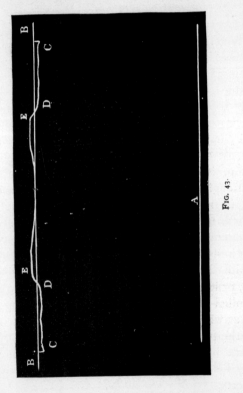

FIG. 43.

this rise of pressure higher than that in the boiler was
not probable, and a test was made of the indicator and
steam-gauge; they were found to agree exactly. It
then appeared evident that the rapid flow of steam to

the steam-chest while steam was being admitted to the cylinder could not be instantly checked, and did not cease until the pressure was increased by 2 pounds.*

The indicator has been of great advantage in bringing about improvements in the construction of pump-cylinders, especially in those for water-works, or for handling large quantities of water. The nearer the diagram from a pump is to a rectangle the better practice it represents. Fig. 44 shows all that can be desired in this respect. The distance from the atmospheric line to the lower line represents the suction, greater or less according to the height the water is lifted and to the freedom with which it passes to the pump. The upper line represents the pressure against the plunger or piston in forcing the water out; this pressure is due to the height to which the water is forced and the friction it encounters.

Beginning with the right-hand lower corner of the diagram, the cylinder being full of water, the pressure rises, as soon as the motion of the plunger begins, to 87 pounds above atmosphere, and continues constant to the end of the stroke, showing that there was no shock due to starting the water-column, and that the passage of the water from the pump-cylinder was practically without resistance. At the very beginning of the return stroke the pressure instantly fell to about 8 pounds below atmosphere, the degree of vacuum re-

---

* Mr. Charles T. Porter was, so far as the writer knows, the first to call attention to this somewhat curious but entirely natural behavior of steam in the steam-chest.

quired to lift the water. The lower or suction-line is

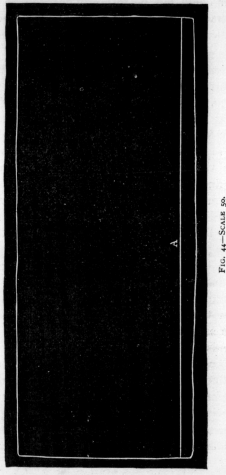

FIG. 44—SCALE 50.

as regular as the upper or discharge-line, showing with
what freedom the water passed the suction-valves.

Such a diagram as this shows an absence of shock to the pump, and that a cylinder full of water is handled. In contradistinction to this diagram, diagrams are often taken from pumps that show enormous shocks

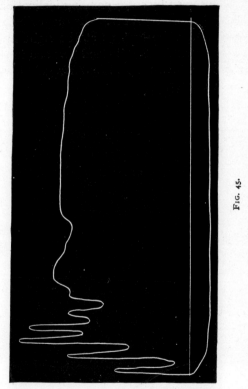

FIG. 45.

to the parts, and only partial filling of the cylinder. Fig. 45 is a fair specimen of what should be avoided. It represents ancient and some modern practice.

If the lines of a pump-diagram enclose a rectangular

figure, it may be assumed that the working of the pump is satisfactory. If there is undue friction of the water in getting into or out of the cylinder it will be greater at some parts of the stroke than at others, and this will be shown by corresponding inclinations of the suction and discharge-lines. If the cylinder is not filled with water, the line, as at the right in Fig. 44, will not be vertical. Shocks and jars and intermittent action will be shown by abrupt irregularities in the lines, as in Fig. 45.

CHAPTER XVII.

STEAM-ENGINE ECONOMY.

GENERAL CONSIDERATIONS.

STEAM-ENGINE economy in a broad sense involves considerations of construction and design, as well as everything that enters into cost of maintenance and operation. With the engineer in charge of engines and boilers, however, the problem is ordinarily that of getting the best possible results from machinery already constructed and placed in his charge. An important part of his education is in the direction of how best to accomplish this end, and the value of his services is largely dependent upon his ability in this direction. Economy to him means keeping down the fuel account, having small bills for repairs, little or no loss from enforced stoppages, maintaining regular speed, and having the least possible loss from deterioration.

The cost of fuel is always an important matter, but sometimes it is of more importance that there be no enforced stoppages, or that the speed be very regular. The engineer must study this in any particular instance, and govern himself according to circumstances.

10

UNDERLOADED ENGINES.

So far as the use of fuel goes, an engineer often finds himself confronted with conditions that render the attaining of good economy impossible. The only course then is to make the best of bad surroundings. The condition unfavorable to fuel economy most likely to be met with is an engine too large for its work. In a non-condensing engine the useless work of moving the piston against the pressure of the atmosphere must always be done. The resistance the piston meets with from the atmosphere being, in round numbers, 15 pounds per square inch, if the mean effective pressure required to do the work is but 15 pounds, then as much work is done in overcoming the atmospheric resistance as is done in overcoming the friction of the parts and doing the useful work. If the load is increased so that the mean effective pressure is 45 pounds, only one third as much work is done against the atmosphere as against the other resistances. One reason, then, and a very important one, why an underloaded engine works with poor economy is that the useless work is too large a fraction of the total work done by the steam. So far only the useless work of overcoming the resistance of the atmosphere has been referred to. There will be, besides this, some further back-pressure which will not increase in proportion as the mean effective pressure is increased, and this, so far as it goes, strengthens the reason just given.

In a condensing-engine the piston has always to be moved against pressure due to imperfect vacuum, and some back-pressure besides, so the same reason holds good, but not to the same extent.

Another reason why poor economy and light loads go together is that part of the work done in the cylinder of a steam engine is done to overcome friction of moving parts, and this friction does not increase as fast as the load is increased; it is sometimes nearly as great with no load as with the engine fairly loaded.

A third reason, which has been previously briefly referred to, is condensation of steam in the cylinder. When ordinary dry steam from the boiler enters the cylinder, cooled by the low temperature during expansion and exhaust, a very material portion of it is condensed, parting with its latent heat to bring up the temperature of the exposed surfaces. In an engine lightly loaded the steam thus condensed is a larger fraction of the total steam used than in one more heavily loaded. The exact loss from condensation cannot from present knowledge of the subject be calculated, or very closely approximated, so that it cannot be told by calculation just what the mean effective pressure on an engine should be for the best economy in fuel-consumption. Experimentally it has been found that with steam from 70 to 90 pounds, by gauge, the best economy in a non-condensing engine obtains when the load is such that cut-off will be not much, if any, earlier than one-quarter stroke. With this cut-off the terminal pressure will be from 5 to 10 pounds above atmosphere. At lower steam-pressure than named the cut-off should be still later. With condensing engines the cut-off may be such that the terminal pressure will be at atmosphere, or a little below.

But the engineer has to do with the engine under-loaded,—too large for the work,—and must consider how he can keep the coal-consumption down without loss in some other direction. When the cut-off is materially before quarter-stroke, so much so that the terminal pressure in a non-condensing engine is below atmosphere, it is in the interest of economy to reduce the speed. This is not, however, always practicable. Sometimes the construction of the engine is such that a change of speed will disarrange the governor to such an extent that the regulation will be poor; in other instances it is merely a matter, so far as the governor is concerned, of a change of a pulley.

Another important consideration in a proposed reduction of speed is the weight of fly-wheel. Good regulation cannot be had with a fly-wheel too light for the work. If the fly-wheel is only of sufficient weight for the speed as it is, if the speed is reduced it will be too light. The momentum of a fly-wheel varies as the diameter and as the square of its revolutions; hence, reducing the speed decreases its capacity rapidly. There are several rules for determining the proper weight of a fly-wheel, the following of which is perhaps as simple as any:

Rule for finding the weight of the *rim* of a fly-wheel for an automatic engine. Multiply 6,000,000 by the indicated horse-power of the engine, and divide the product by the diameter of the wheel in feet multiplied by the square of its number of revolutions per minute.

Take, for example, an engine developing 75 indicated horse-power, having a fly-wheel pulley 14 feet diameter, running 80 revolutions per minute: what should be the weight of metal in the rim of the wheel? 6,000,000 × 75 = 450,000,000; the square of 80 is 80 × 80 = 6400, and 6400 × 14 = 89,600. Then 450,000,000 ÷ 89,600 = 5022 pounds for the weight of the rim of the wheel.

Some builders use a larger constant than 6,000,000, which gives greater weight of wheel, but more use a smaller constant. The rule, as given above, gives very regular turning, and may be safely employed by the engineer. Cast-iron weighs about .26 pound per cubic inch; so by finding the cubic inches in the rim of the wheel, and multiplying by this decimal (.26), the weight will be found with reasonable exactness; then finding by the use of the indicator the horse-power developed, it can be told whether the speed can be decreased with satisfactory results without increasing the weight of wheel. For full-stroke engines a wheel of three fourths the weight, as above found, will generally answer the requirements. The diameter of the wheel may, if a fly-wheel pulley is used, be measured from the outside. Where a square-rimmed wheel is used the diameter should be measured from the centre of the rim, so as to get the mean of the outside and inside diameters.

In some instances, where close regulation and even turning are not very essential, the speed may be reduced so as to bring the fly-wheel proportion considerably less than found by the rule given. Judgment must be used in considering this. In other instances a plain fly-wheel may be placed beside the fly-wheel pulley.

WORKING WITH LOWER STEAM PRESSURE.

Reducing the speed is usually the only practical means of increasing the economy of fuel-consumption in an underloaded non-condensing engine. By this means the useless work done against the pressure of the atmosphere is diminished, the inevitable loss from filling the clearance-space with steam at every stroke is less, because the number of times this space is filled, per minute or per hour, is less, and friction is generally reduced. A slight saving may sometimes be effected by working with reduced steam-pressure; but what it will amount to, if anything, can only be told by trial. It will depend upon the steaming qualities of the boiler under the higher and the lower pressures; upon the construction of the engine, particularly as to whether the valves work under full pressure or are wholly or partially balanced; upon whether leakage will be less at low-pressure; and upon a variety of conditions that cannot well be enumerated. Usually in a well-constructed engine, unless expansion is considerably—say 2 or 3 pounds at least—below the atmosphere, working with lower boiler-pressure will not decrease the coal-consumption. If advisable to reduce the initial pressure, better results will usually follow a small amount of throttling, keeping the boiler-pressure as it is. Reducing the boiler-pressure in the instance of an underloaded condensing-engine is much more likely to save fuel than in one worked non-condensing. In any case, as previously intimated, the effect can only be known by trial. Weighing the coal used running both ways will settle the matter conclusively.

OVERLOADED ENGINES.

If an engine is overloaded the remedy that most naturally suggests itself is to increase the speed. The diagram will show, by the freedom with which the steam gets into and out of the cylinder, whether in this respect higher speed is advisable, or will accomplish the end sought. If initial pressure is nearly equal to boiler-pressure, with only a pound or two of back-pressure, then there will be no trouble in increasing the speed from 10 to 20 per cent, if the wearing and moving parts can be run faster without danger or inconvenience. If the diagram shows that the steam-passages are small for the present speed, then but little will be gained in the way of additional power by increasing the speed, while there may be a loss in economy of fuel. Increasing the speed of an engine ought to improve the regulation, because it increases the capacity of the fly-wheel.

WORKING WITH HIGHER STEAM-PRESSURE.

Frequently the very best remedy for an overloaded engine is increasing the steam-pressure. Doing this of course involves previous considerations of the strength of the boiler, and of various parts of the engine, as well as the amplitude of the wearing surfaces to resist the higher pressure. When there are no objections to increasing the pressure, doing so generally increases economy, for reasons previously explained.

ADDING A CONDENSER.

Another plan for helping out an overloaded non-condensing engine is to add a condenser. Where fairly high pressure of steam is carried—say, not less than 75 pounds gauge-pressure—and the cut-off is from one-quarter to one-third stroke, a condenser will, by adding from 9 to 11 pounds pressure below atmosphere, shorten the cut-off, and the economy will be increased. Adding a condenser to a lightly-loaded engine working with high steam-pressure, in the expectation of saving coal, as is frequently done, will generally end in disappointment. Condensation in the cylinder will be in-increased, and colder feed must be used, the two frequently neutralizing all that is otherwise gained by the use of the condenser.

When, from any cause, it is necessary to materially reduce the steam-pressure carried, thus in effect making the engine small for the work, then a condenser is a valuable addition.

HEATING FEED-WATER.

In a non-condensing engine advantage should always be taken of heating the feed-water by the exhaust-steam. In this way a saving of coal equal to from 10 to 15 per cent will be effected, besides which it is much better for the boiler to feed hot water. With a condensing-engine there is very little gain from the use of a heater, provided the temperature of the hot-well is not unnecessarily low.

CHAPTER XVIII.

TABLES.

TABLE I.

AREAS OF CIRCLES IN SQUARE INCHES.

Diameter in inches.	Area in square inches.	Diameter in inches.	Area in square inches.	Diameter in inches.	Area in square inches.
$\frac{1}{64}$	.000192	$1\frac{11}{16}$	2.2365	$4\frac{7}{8}$	18.666
$\frac{1}{32}$	.000767	$1\frac{3}{4}$	2.4053	5	19.635
$\frac{1}{16}$	.003068	$1\frac{13}{16}$	2.5801	$5\frac{1}{8}$	20.629
$\frac{1}{8}$	.012272	$1\frac{7}{8}$	2.7612	$5\frac{1}{4}$	21.648
$\frac{3}{16}$	.02761	$1\frac{15}{16}$	2.9483	$5\frac{3}{8}$	22.691
$\frac{1}{4}$	.04908	2	3.1416	$5\frac{1}{2}$	23.758
$\frac{5}{16}$	.07670	$2\frac{1}{8}$	3.5466	$5\frac{5}{8}$	24.851
$\frac{3}{8}$	.11045	$2\frac{1}{4}$	3.9761	$5\frac{3}{4}$	25.967
$\frac{7}{16}$	.15033	$2\frac{3}{8}$	4.4301	$5\frac{7}{8}$	27.109
$\frac{1}{2}$	.19635	$2\frac{1}{2}$	4.9087	6	28.274
$\frac{9}{16}$	.24851	$2\frac{5}{8}$	5.4119	$6\frac{1}{8}$	29.465
$\frac{5}{8}$	.30680	$2\frac{3}{4}$	5.9396	$6\frac{1}{4}$	30.679
$\frac{11}{16}$	.37122	$2\frac{7}{8}$	6.4918	$6\frac{3}{8}$	31.919
$\frac{3}{4}$	.44179	3	7.0686	$6\frac{1}{2}$	33.183
$\frac{13}{16}$	.51849	$3\frac{1}{8}$	7.6699	$6\frac{5}{8}$	34.472
$\frac{7}{8}$	.60132	$3\frac{1}{4}$	8.2958	$6\frac{3}{4}$	35.785
$\frac{15}{16}$	.69029	$3\frac{3}{8}$	8.9462	$6\frac{7}{8}$	37.122
1	.7854	$3\frac{1}{2}$	9.6211	7	38.485
$1\frac{1}{16}$	.88664	$3\frac{5}{8}$	10.3210	$7\frac{1}{8}$	39.871
$1\frac{1}{8}$	.99402	$3\frac{3}{4}$	11.0447	$7\frac{1}{4}$	41.283
$1\frac{3}{16}$	1.1075	$3\frac{7}{8}$	11.7933	$7\frac{3}{8}$	42.718
$1\frac{1}{4}$	1.2272	4	12.566	$7\frac{1}{2}$	44.179
$1\frac{5}{16}$	1.3530	$4\frac{1}{8}$	13.364	$7\frac{5}{8}$	45.664
$1\frac{3}{8}$	1.4849	$4\frac{1}{4}$	14.186	$7\frac{3}{4}$	47.173
$1\frac{7}{16}$	1.6229	$4\frac{3}{8}$	15.033	$7\frac{7}{8}$	48.707
$1\frac{1}{2}$	1.7671	$4\frac{1}{2}$	15.904	8	50.266
$1\frac{9}{16}$	1.9175	$4\frac{5}{8}$	16.800	$8\frac{1}{8}$	51.849
$1\frac{5}{8}$	2.0739	$4\frac{3}{4}$	17.721	$8\frac{1}{4}$	53.456

TABLE I.—Continued.

Diameter in inches.	Area in square inches.	Diameter in inches.	Area in square inches.	Diameter in inches.	Area in square inches.
8 3/8	55.088	13 3/4	148.490	19 1/8	287.272
8 1/2	56.745	13 7/8	151.201	19 1/4	291.040
8 5/8	58.426	14	153.938	19 3/8	294.832
8 3/4	60.132	14 1/8	156.700	19 1/2	298.648
8 7/8	61.862	14 1/4	159.485	19 5/8	302.489
9	63.617	14 3/8	162.296	19 3/4	306.355
9 1/8	65.397	14 1/2	165.130	19 7/8	310.245
9 1/4	67.201	14 5/8	167.990	20	314.16
9 3/8	69.029	14 3/4	170.874	20 1/8	318.10
9 1/2	70.882	14 7/8	173.782	20 1/4	322.06
9 5/8	72.760	15	176.715	20 3/8	326.05
9 3/4	74.662	15 1/8	179.673	20 1/2	330.06
9 7/8	76.589	15 1/4	182.655	20 5/8	334.10
10	78.540	15 3/8	185.660	20 3/4	338.16
10 1/8	80.516	15 1/2	188.692	20 7/8	342.25
10 1/4	82.516	15 5/8	191.748	21	346.36
10 3/8	84.541	15 3/4	194.828	21 1/8	350.50
10 1/2	86.590	15 7/8	197.933	21 1/4	354.66
10 5/8	88.664	16	201.062	21 3/8	358.84
10 3/4	90.763	16 1/8	204.216	21 1/2	363.05
10 7/8	92.886	16 1/4	207.395	21 5/8	367.28
11	95.033	16 3/8	210.598	21 3/4	371.54
11 1/8	97.205	16 1/2	213.825	21 7/8	375.83
11 1/4	99.402	16 5/8	217.077	22	380.13
11 3/8	101.623	16 3/4	220.354	22 1/8	384.47
11 1/2	103.869	16 7/8	223.655	22 1/4	388.82
11 5/8	106.139	17	226.981	22 3/8	393.20
11 3/4	108.434	17 1/8	230.331	22 1/2	397.61
11 7/8	110.754	17 1/4	233.706	22 5/8	402.04
12	113.098	17 3/8	237.105	22 3/4	406.49
12 1/8	115.467	17 1/2	240.529	22 7/8	410.97
12 1/4	117.859	17 5/8	243.977	23	415.48
12 3/8	120.277	17 3/4	247.450	23 1/8	420.00
12 1/2	122.719	17 7/8	250.948	23 1/4	424.56
12 5/8	125.185	18	254.470	23 3/8	429.13
12 3/4	127.677	18 1/8	258.016	23 1/2	433.74
12 7/8	130.192	18 1/4	261.587	23 5/8	438.36
13	132.733	18 3/8	265.183	23 3/4	443.01
13 1/8	135.297	18 1/2	268.803	23 7/8	447.69
13 1/4	137.887	18 5/8	272.448	24	452.39
13 3/8	140.501	18 3/4	276.117	24 1/8	457.11
13 1/2	143.139	18 7/8	279.811	24 1/4	461.86
13 5/8	145.802	19	283.529	24 3/8	466.64

TABLE I.—*Continued.*

Diameter in inches.	Area in square inches.	Diameter in inches.	Area in square inches	Diameter in inches.	Area in square inches.
24½	471.44	29⅞	700.98	35¼	975.91
24⅝	476.26	30	706.86	35⅜	982.84
24¾	481.11	30⅛	712.76	35½	989.80
24⅞	485.98	30¼	718.69	35⅝	996.78
25	490.87	30⅜	724.64	35¾	1003.79
25⅛	495.80	30½	730.62	35⅞	1010.82
25¼	500.74	30⅝	736.62	36	1017.88
25⅜	505.71	30¾	742.64	36⅛	1024.96
25½	510.71	30⅞	748.69	36¼	1032.06
25⅝	515.73	31	754.77	36⅜	1039.19
25¾	520.78	31⅛	760.87	36½	1046.35
25⅞	525.84	31¼	766.99	36⅝	1053.53
26	530.93	31⅜	773.14	36¾	1060.73
26⅛	536.05	31½	779.31	36⅞	1067.96
26¼	541.19	31⅝	785.51	37	1075.21
26⅜	546.36	31¾	791.73	37⅛	1082.50
26½	551.55	31⅞	797.98	37¼	1089.79
26⅝	556.76	32	804.25	37⅜	1097.11
26¾	562.00	32⅛	810.54	37½	1104.47
26⅞	567.27	32¼	816.86	37⅝	1111.84
27	572 56	32⅜	823.21	37¾	1119.24
27⅛	577.87	32½	829.58	37⅞	1126.67
27¼	583.21	32⅝	835.97	38	1134.12
27⅜	588.57	32¾	842.39	38⅛	1141.59
27½	593.96	32⅞	848.83	38¼	1149.09
27⅝	599.37	33	855.30	38⅜	1156.61
27¾	604.81	33⅛	861.79	38½	1164.16
27⅞	610.27	33¼	868.31	38⅝	1171.73
28	615.75	33⅜	874.85	38¾	1179.33
28⅛	621.26	33½	881.41	38⅞	1186.95
28¼	626.80	33⅝	888.00	39	1194.59
28⅜	632.36	33¾	894.62	39⅛	1202.26
28½	637.94	33⅞	901.26	39¼	1209.96
28⅝	643.55	34	907.92	39⅜	1217.68
28¾	649.18	34⅛	914.61	39½	1225.42
28⅞	654.84	34¼	921.32	39⅝	1233.19
29	660.52	34⅜	928.06	39¾	1240.98
29⅛	666.23	34½	934.82	39⅞	1248.80
29¼	671.96	34⅝	941.61	40	1256.64
29⅜	677.71	34¾	948.42	40⅛	1264.51
29½	683.49	34⅞	955.25	40¼	1272.40
29⅝	689.30	35	962.11	40⅜	1280.31
29¾	695.13	35⅛	969.00	40½	1288.25

INDICATOR PRACTICE.

TABLE I—*Continued.*

Diameter in inches.	Area in square inches.	Diameter in inches.	Area in square inches.	Diameter in inches.	Area in square inches.
$40\frac{5}{8}$	1296.22	46	1661.91	$52\frac{3}{4}$	2185.42
$40\frac{3}{4}$	1304.21	$46\frac{1}{8}$	1670.95	53	2206.18
$40\frac{7}{8}$	1312.22	$46\frac{1}{4}$	1680.02	$53\frac{1}{4}$	2227.05
41	1320.26	$46\frac{3}{8}$	1689.11	$53\frac{1}{2}$	2248.01
$41\frac{1}{8}$	1328.32	$46\frac{1}{2}$	1698.23	$53\frac{3}{4}$	2269.07
$41\frac{1}{4}$	1336.41	$46\frac{5}{8}$	1707.37	54	2290.22
$41\frac{3}{8}$	1344.52	$46\frac{3}{4}$	1716.54	$54\frac{1}{4}$	2311.48
$41\frac{1}{2}$	1352.66	$46\frac{7}{8}$	1725.73	$54\frac{1}{2}$	2332.84
$41\frac{5}{8}$	1360.82	47	1734.95	$54\frac{3}{4}$	2354.29
$41\frac{3}{4}$	1369.00	$47\frac{1}{8}$	1744.19	55	2375.83
$41\frac{7}{8}$	1377.21	$47\frac{1}{4}$	1753.45	$55\frac{1}{4}$	2397.48
42	1385.45	$47\frac{3}{8}$	1762.74	$55\frac{1}{2}$	2419.23
$42\frac{1}{8}$	1393.70	$47\frac{1}{2}$	1772.06	$55\frac{3}{4}$	2441.07
$42\frac{1}{4}$	1401.99	$47\frac{5}{8}$	1781.40	56	2463.01
$42\frac{3}{8}$	1410.30	$47\frac{3}{4}$	1790.76	$56\frac{1}{4}$	2485.05
$42\frac{1}{2}$	1418.63	$47\frac{7}{8}$	1800.15	$56\frac{1}{2}$	2507.19
$42\frac{5}{8}$	1426.99	48	1809.56	$56\frac{3}{4}$	2529.43
$42\frac{3}{4}$	1435.37	$48\frac{1}{8}$	1819.00	57	2551.76
$42\frac{7}{8}$	1443.77	$48\frac{1}{4}$	1828.46	$57\frac{1}{4}$	2574.20
43	1452.20	$48\frac{3}{8}$	1837.95	$57\frac{1}{2}$	2596.73
$43\frac{1}{8}$	1460.66	$48\frac{1}{2}$	1847.46	$57\frac{3}{4}$	2619.36
$43\frac{1}{4}$	1469.14	$48\frac{5}{8}$	1856.99	58	2642.08
$43\frac{3}{8}$	1477.64	$48\frac{3}{4}$	1866.55	$58\frac{1}{4}$	2664.91
$43\frac{1}{2}$	1486.17	$48\frac{7}{8}$	1876.14	$58\frac{1}{2}$	2687.84
$43\frac{5}{8}$	1494.73	49	1885.75	$58\frac{3}{4}$	2710.86
$43\frac{3}{4}$	1503.30	$49\frac{1}{8}$	1895.38	59	2733.97
$43\frac{7}{8}$	1511.91	$49\frac{1}{4}$	1905.04	$59\frac{1}{4}$	2757.20
44	1520.53	$49\frac{3}{8}$	1914.72	$59\frac{1}{2}$	2780.51
$44\frac{1}{8}$	1529.19	$49\frac{1}{2}$	1924.43	$59\frac{3}{4}$	2803.93
$44\frac{1}{4}$	1537.86	$49\frac{5}{8}$	1934.16	60	2827.44
$44\frac{3}{8}$	1546.56	$49\frac{3}{4}$	1943.91	$60\frac{1}{4}$	2851.05
$44\frac{1}{2}$	1555.29	$49\frac{7}{8}$	1953.69	$60\frac{1}{2}$	2874.76
$44\frac{5}{8}$	1564.04	50	1963.50	$60\frac{3}{4}$	2898.57
$44\frac{3}{4}$	1572.81	$50\frac{1}{4}$	1983.18	61	2922.47
$44\frac{7}{8}$	1581.61	$50\frac{1}{2}$	2002.96	$61\frac{1}{4}$	2946.48
45	1590.43	$50\frac{3}{4}$	2022.86	$61\frac{1}{2}$	2970.58
$45\frac{1}{8}$	1599.28	51	2042.82	$61\frac{3}{4}$	2994.78
$45\frac{1}{4}$	1608.16	$51\frac{1}{4}$	2062.90	62	3019.08
$45\frac{3}{8}$	1617.05	$51\frac{1}{2}$	2083.08	$62\frac{1}{4}$	3043.47
$45\frac{1}{2}$	1625.97	$51\frac{3}{4}$	2103.35	$62\frac{1}{2}$	3067.97
$45\frac{5}{8}$	1634.92	52	2123.72	$62\frac{3}{4}$	3092.56
$45\frac{3}{4}$	1643.89	$52\frac{1}{4}$	2144.18	63	3117.25
$45\frac{7}{8}$	1652.89	$52\frac{1}{2}$	2164.76	$63\frac{1}{4}$	3142.04

TABLE I.—*Continued.*

Diameter in inches.	Area in square inches.	Diameter in inches.	Area in square inches.	Diameter in inches.	Area in square inches.
63½	3166.93	74¼	4329.96	85	5674.51
63¾	3191.91	74½	4359.17	85¼	5707.94
64	3217.00	74¾	4388.47	85½	5741.47
64¼	3242.18	75	4417.87	85¾	5775.10
64½	3267.46	75¼	4447.38	86	5808.82
64¾	3292.84	75½	4476.98	86¼	5842.64
65	3318.31	75¾	4506.67	86½	5876.56
65¼	3343.86	76	4536.47	86¾	5910.58
65½	3369.56	76¼	4566.36	87	5944.69
65¾	3395.33	76½	4596.36	87¼	5978.91
66	3421.20	76¾	4626.45	87½	6013.22
66¼	3447.17	77	4656.64	87¾	6047.63
66½	3473.24	77¼	4686.92	88	6082.14
66¾	3499.40	77½	4717.31	88¼	6116.74
67	3525.66	77¾	4747.79	88½	6151.45
67¼	3552.02	78	4778.37	88¾	6186.25
67½	3578.48	78¼	4809.05	89	6221.15
67¾	3605.04	78½	4839.83	89¼	6256.15
68	3631.69	78¾	4870.71	89½	6291.25
68¼	3658.44	79	4901.68	89¾	6326.45
68½	3685.29	79¼	4932.75	90	6361.74
68¾	3712.24	79½	4963.92	90¼	6397.13
69	3739.29	79¾	4995.19	90½	6432.62
69¼	3766.43	80	5026.56	90¾	6468.21
69½	3793.68	80¼	5058.03	91	6503.90
69¾	3821.02	80½	5089.59	91¼	6539.68
70	3848.46	80¾	5121.25	91½	6575.56
70¼	3876.00	81	5153.01	91¾	6611.55
70½	3903.63	81¼	5184.87	92	6647.63
70¾	3931.37	81½	5216.82	92¼	6683.80
71	3959.20	81¾	5248.88	92½	6720.08
71¼	3987.13	82	5281.03	92¾	6756.45
71½	4015.16	82¼	5313.28	93	6792.92
71¾	4043.29	82½	5345.63	93¼	6829.49
72	4071.51	82¾	5378.08	93½	6866.16
72¼	4099.84	83	5410.62	93¾	6902.93
72½	4128.26	83¼	5443.26	94	6939.79
72¾	4156.78	83½	5476.01	94¼	6976.76
73	4185.40	83¾	5508.84	94½	7013.82
73¼	4214.11	84	5541.78	94¾	7050.98
73½	4242.93	84¼	5574.82	95	7088.24
73¾	4271.84	84½	5607.95	95¼	7125.59
74	4300.85	84¾	5641.18	95½	7163.04

TABLE I.—*Continued.*

Diameter in inches.	Area in square inches.	Diameter in inches.	Area in square inches.	Diameter in inches.	Area in square inches.
95¾	7200.60	97¼	7427.97	98¾	7658.88
96	7238.25	97½	7466.21	99	7697.71
96¼	7275.99	97¾	7504.55	99¼	7736.63
96½	7313.84	98	7542.98	99½	7775.66
96¾	7351.79	98¼	7581.52	99¾	7814.78
97	7389.83	98½	7620.15	100	7854.00

The area of a circle larger than in the table may be found by squaring the diameter and multiplying the product by the decimal .7854; but it may generally be more easily found by the use of the table. Thus, to find the area of a circle 120 inches = 10 feet diameter, find in the table the area of a circle 10 inches diameter and multiply by 144, the number of square inches in a foot. The area of a 10-inch circle is 78.54 square inches, and of a 10-foot circle 78.54 square feet, or 78.54 × 144 = 11309.76 square inches. Again, the areas of circles vary as the squares of their diameters; hence, to find the area of, say, a circle 150 inches diameter, find in the table the area of a 75-inch circle and multiply by 4; or find the area of a 50-inch circle and multiply by 9.

TABLE II.

PROPERTIES OF SATURATED STEAM.

(Abridged from Tables calculated by Charles T. Porter.)

Absolute pressure in pounds per square inch	Temperature in degrees, Fahrenheit.	Heat-units per pound reckoning from zero.	Heat-units per pound contained in the water.	Weight in decimals of a pound per cubic foot.	Specific volume.
1	102	1145	102.1	.0030	20620
2	126.3	1152.5	126.4	.0058	10720
3	141.6	1157.1	141.9	.0085	7326
4	153.1	1160.6	153.4	.0112	5600
5	162.3	1163.4	162.7	.0137	4535
6	170.1	1165.8	170.6	.0163	3814
7	176.9	1167.9	177.4	.0189	3300
8	182.9	1169.7	183.5	.0214	2910
9	188.3	1171.4	188.9	.0239	2607
10	193.2	1172.9	193.9	.0264	2360
11	197.8	1174.2	198.5	.0289	2157
12	202	1175.5	202.7	.0313	1988
13	205.9	1176.7	206.7	.0337	1846
14	209.6	1177.9	210.4	.0362	1722
14.7	212	1178.6	212.9	.0380	1644
15	213.1	1178.9	213.9	.0387	1612
16	216.3	1179.9	217.2	.0413	1514
17	219.4	1180.9	220.4	.0437	1427
18	222.4	1181.8	223.4	.0462	1351
19	225.2	1182.6	226.3	.0487	1282.1
20	227.9	1183.5	229	.0511	1220.3
21	230.5	1184.2	231.7	.0536	1164.4
22	233	1185	234.2	.0561	1113.5
23	235.4	1185.7	236.7	.0585	1066.9
24	237.7	1186.5	239	.0610	1024.1
25	240	1187.1	241.3	.0634	984.8
26	242.2	1187.8	243.5	.0658	948.4
27	244.3	1188.5	245.7	.0683	914.6
28	246.3	1189	247.7	.0707	883.2
29	248.3	1189.7	249.8	.0731	854
30	250.2	1190.3	251.7	.0755	826.8
31	252.1	1190.8	253.6	.0779	801.2
32	254	1191.4	255.5	.0803	777.2
33	255.7	1191.9	257.3	.0827	754.7

TABLE II.— *Continued.*

Absolute pressure in pounds per square inch.	Temperature in degrees, Fahrenheit.	Heat-units per pound, reckoning from zero.	Heat-units per pound contained in the water.	Weight in decimals of a pound per cubic foot.	Specific volume.
34	257.5	1192.5	259.1	.0851	733.5
35	259.2	1193	260.8	.0875	713.4
36	260.9	1193.5	262.5	.0899	694.5
37	262.5	1194	264.2	.0922	676.6
38	264	1194.5	265.8	.0946	659.7
39	265.6	1195	267.4	.0970	643.6
40	267.1	1195.4	268.9	.0994	628.2
41	268.6	1195.9	270.5	.1017	613.4
42	270.1	1196.3	272	.1041	599.3
43	271.5	1196.7	273.4	.1064	586.1
44	272.9	1197.2	274.9	.1088	573.7
45	274.3	1197.6	276.3	.1111	561.8
46	275.7	1198	277.7	.1134	550.4
47	277	1198.4	279	.1158	539.5
48	278.3	1198.8	280.4	.1181	529
49	279.6	1199.2	281.7	.1204	518.6
50	280.9	1199.6	283	.1227	508.5
51	282.1	1200	284.2	.1251	499.1
52	283.3	1200.4	285.5	.1274	490.1
53	284.5	1200.7	286.7	.1297	481.4
54	285.7	1201.1	288	.1320	472.9
55	286.9	1201.4	289.2	.1343	464.7
56	288.1	1201.8	290.3	.1366	457
57	289.1	1202.1	291.5	.1388	449.6
58	290.3	1202.5	292.7	.1411	442.4
59	291.4	1202.8	293.8	.1434	435.3
60	292.5	1203.2	294.9	.1457	428.5
61	293.6	1203.5	296	.1479	422
62	294.7	1203.8	297.1	.1502	415.6
63	295.7	1204.1	298.2	.1525	409.4
64	296.8	1204.5	299.2	.1547	403.5
65	297.8	1204.8	300.3	.1570	397.7
66	298.8	1205.1	301.3	.1592	392.1
67	299.8	1205.4	302.4	.1615	386.6
68	300.8	1205.7	303.4	.1637	381.3
69	301.8	1206	304.4	.1660	376.1
70	302.7	1206.3	305.4	.1682	371.2
71	303.7	1206.6	306.4	.1704	366.4
72	304.6	1206.9	307.3	.1726	361.7
73	305.6	1207.1	308.3	.1748	357.1
74	306.5	1207.4	309.3	.1770	352.6

TABLE II.—*Continued.*

Absolute pressure in pounds per square inch.	Temperature in degrees, Fahrenheit.	Heat-units per pound, reckoning from zero.	Heat-units per pound contained in the water.	Weight in decimals of a pound per cubic foot.	Specific volume.
75	307.4	1207.7	310.2	.1792	348.3
76	308.3	1208	311.1	.1814	344.1
77	309.2	1208.2	312	.1836	340
78	310.1	1208.5	313	.1858	336
79	310.9	1208.8	313.8	.1880	332.1
80	311.8	1209	314.7	.1901	328.3
81	312.7	1209.3	315.6	.1923	324.6
82	313.5	1209.6	316.5	.1945	320.9
83	314.4	1209.8	317.3	.1967	317.3
84	315.2	1210	318.2	.1989	313.9
85	316	1210.3	319	.2010	310.5
86	316.8	1210.6	319.9	.2032	307.2
87	317.6	1210.8	320.7	.2053	304
88	318.5	1211	321.5	.2075	300.8
89	319.3	1211.3	322.4	.2097	297.7
90	320	1211.6	323.2	.2118	294.7
91	320.8	1211.8	324	.2139	291.8
92	321.6	1212	324.8	.2161	288.9
93	322.4	1212.3	325.6	.2183	286.1
94	323.1	1212.5	326.4	.2204	283.3
95	323.9	1212.7	327.1	.2225	280.6
96	324.6	1213	327.9	.2245	278
97	325.4	1213.2	328.7	.2267	275.4
98	326.1	1213.4	329.4	.2288	272.8
99	326.8	1213.6	330.2	.2309	270.3
100	327.6	1213.8	331	.2330	267.9
101	328.3	1214	331.7	.2351	265.5
102	329	1214.3	332.4	.2372	263.2
103	329.7	1214.5	333.1	.2392	260.9
104	330.4	1214.7	333.9	.2413	258.7
105	331.1	1214.9	334.6	.2434	256.5
106	331.8	1215.1	335.3	.2455	254.3
107	332.5	1215.3	336	.2475	252.2
108	333.2	1215.6	336.7	.2496	250.1
109	333.9	1215.8	337.4	.2517	248
110	334.5	1216	338.1	.2538	246
111	335.2	1216.2	338.8	.2558	244
112	335.9	1216.4	339.5	.2579	242
113	336.5	1216.6	340.2	.2599	240.1
114	337.2	1216.8	340.8	.2620	238.2
115	337.8	1217	341.5	.2640	236.3
116	338.5	1217.2	342.2	.2661	234.5

TABLE II.—Continued.

Absolute pressure in pounds per square inch.	Temperature in degrees, Fahrenheit.	Heat-units per pound, reckoning from zero.	Heat units per pound contained in the water.	Weight in decimals of a pound per cubic foot.	Specific volume.
117	339.1	1217.4	342.8	.2682	232.7
118	339.7	1217.6	343.5	.2702	231
119	340.4	1217.8	344.2	.2722	229.3
120	341	1217.9	344.8	.2743	227.6
121	341.6	1218.1	345.4	.2763	226
122	342.2	1218.3	346.1	.2783	224.4
123	342.9	1218.5	346.7	.2803	222.8
124	343.5	1218.7	347.3	.2823	221.2
125	344.1	1218.9	348	.2843	219.7
126	344.7	1219.1	348.6	.2862	218.2
127	345.3	1219.3	349.2	.2882	216.7
128	345.9	1219.4	349.8	.2902	215.2
129	346.5	1219.6	350.4	.2922	213.7
130	347.1	1219.8	351.1	.2942	212.3
131	347.6	1220	351.7	.2962	210.9
132	348.2	1220.2	352.3	.2982	209.5
133	348.8	1220.4	352.9	.3001	208.1
134	349.4	1220.5	353.5	.3021	206.7
135	350	1220.7	354.1	.3040	205.4
136	350.5	1220.9	354.6	.3060	204.1
137	351.1	1221	355.2	.3080	202.8
138	351.7	1221.2	355.8	.3099	201.5
139	352.2	1221.4	356.4	.3119	200.2
140	352.8	1221.5	357	.3139	199
141	353.3	1221.7	357.5	.3159	197.8
142	353.9	1221.9	358.1	.3179	196.6
143	354.4	1222	358.7	.3199	195.4
144	355	1222.2	359.2	.3219	194.2
145	355.5	1222.4	359.8	.3239	193
146	356	1222.5	360.4	.3259	191.9
147	356.6	1222.7	360.9	.3279	190.8
148	357.1	1222.9	361.5	.3299	189.7
149	357.6	1223	362	.3320	188.6
150	358.1	1223.2	362.6	.3340	187.5
151	358.7	1223.3	363.1	.3358	186.4
152	359.2	1223.5	363.6	.3376	185.3
153	359.7	1223.7	364.2	.3394	184.3
154	360.2	1223.9	364.7	.3412	183.3
155	360.7	1224	365.2	.3430	182.3
156	361.2	1224.1	365.8	.3448	181.3
157	361.8	1224.3	366.3	.3467	180.3
158	362.3	1224.4	366.8	.3485	179.3

TABLE II.—*Continued.*

Absolute pressure in pounds per square inch.	Temperature in degrees, Fahrenheit.	Heat-units per pound, reckoning from zero.	Heat-units per pound contained in the water.	Weight in decimals of a pound per cubic foot.	Specific volume.
159	362.8	1224.6	367.3	.3503	178.3
160	363.3	1224.8	367.9	.3521	177.3
161	363.8	1224.9	368.4	.3540	176.4
162	364.3	1225	368.9	.3558	175.5
163	364.8	1225.2	369.4	.3577	174.6
164	365.2	1225.3	369.9	.3596	173.7
165	365.7	1225.5	370.4	.3615	172.8
166	366.2	1225.6	370.9	.3634	171.9
167	366.7	1225.8	371.4	.3652	171
168	367.2	1225.9	371.9	.3671	170.1
169	367.7	1226.1	372.4	.3690	169.2
170	368.2	1226.2	372.9	.3709	168.4
171	368.6	1226.4	373.4	.3727	167.6
172	369.1	1226.5	373.9	.3745	166.8
173	369.6	1226.7	374.4	.3763	166
174	370	1226.8	374.9	.3781	165.2
175	370.5	1226 9	375.4	.3799	164.4
176	371	1227.1	375.9	.3817	163.6
177	371.4	1227.2	376.3	.3835	162.8
178	371.9	1227.4	376.8	.3853	162
179	372.4	1227.5	377.3	.3871	161.2
180	372.8	1227.7	377.8	.3889	160.4
181	373.3	1227.8	378.3	.3908	159.7
182	373.7	1227.9	378.7	.3926	159
183	374.2	1228.1	379.2	.3944	158.3
184	374.6	1228.2	379.7	.3962	157.6
185	375.1	1228.3	380.1	.3981	156.9
186	375.5	1228.5	380.6	.3999	156.2
187	376	1228.6	381.1	.4017	155.5
188	376.4	1228.7	381.5	.4036	154.8
189	376.9	1228.9	382	.4054	154.1
190	377.3	1229	382.4	.4072	153.4
191	377.7	1229.1	382.9	.4090	152.7
192	378.2	1229.3	383.3	.4108	152
193	378.6	1229.4	383.8	.4125	151.3
194	379	1229.5	384.2	.4143	150.7
195	379.5	1229.7	384.7	.4160	150.1
196	380	1229.8	385.1	.4178	149.5
197	380.3	1229.9	385.6	.4196	148.9
198	380.7	1230.1	386	.4214	148.3
199	381.1	1230.2	386.5	.4232	147.7
200	381.6	1230.3	386.9	.4250	147.1

In Table II. the column of temperature is the temperature, or sensible heat of steam, and the water with which it is in contact.

Under Specific Volume is given the volume of steam at different pressures as compared with water. Thus, at 80 pounds absolute pressure steam occupies space 328.3 greater than water.

The heat-units contained in water at temperatures less than 102°, the lowest given in the table, may, without material error, be taken as the same as the temperature of the water.

The latent heat of steam is not given in the table, but may be readily found by subtracting the heat-units contained in the water from those contained in the steam. As, for example, steam at 90 pounds absolute pressure contains 1211.6, and water of a corresponding temperature 323.2 heat-units. Subtract the last-named number from the first, and the remainder is 888.4, which is the latent heat of steam at that pressure.

ECONOMY OF HEATING FEED-WATER.

Suppose the feed-water is at a temperature of 60°, and boiler-pressure 70 pounds, what would be the gain due to heating the water by exhaust-steam to a temperature of 202°? Seventy pounds pressure by gauge is (about) 85 pounds absolute. From the table the total heat of 1 pound of steam of that pressure is found to be 1210.3 heat-units. The water contains 60 units, leaving to be imparted 1210.3 − 60 = 1150.3. In the heater 202.7 − 60 = 142.7 heat-units are imparted to the pound of water, a saving by the use of the heater of 142.7 ÷ 1150.3 = 12 + per cent.

THE EVAPORATIVE DUTY OF BOILERS.

The evaporative duty of boilers is usually given from and at 212°, in which the heat required to vaporize the water from that temperature, and under the pressure of the atmosphere, is accounted for. By the use of Table II. the evaporation from any temperature of feed-water, and at any pressure up to 200 pounds per square inch, can be reduced to standard evaporation. Suppose a boiler is evaporating 8 pounds of water of a temperature of 50° into steam of an absolute pressure of 100 pounds, what is the equivalent evaporation from and at 212°? The heat-units per pound of steam of 100 pounds pressure are 1213.8, which, less 50 contained in the water, leaves 1163.8 to be imparted. The heat units in steam of 212° temperature is, by the table, 1178.6, and of the water 212.9. To evaporate water from and at 212° requires then 1178.6 — 212.9 = 965.7 heat-units per pound. Multiplying the actual evaporation, 8 pounds, by 1163.8, and dividing by 965.7, we have 9.64 pounds as the equivalent evaporation from and at 212°.

TABLE III.

HYPERBOLIC LOGARITHMS + 1.

Number.	Hyperbolic Log. + 1.	Number.	Hyperbolic Log. + 1.	Number.	Hyperbolic Log. + 1.	Number.	Hyp'bolic Log. + 1.
1.1	1.095	4.4	2.482	7.7	3.041	20	3.996
1.2	1.182	4.5	2.504	7.8	3.054	21	4.045
1.3	1.262	4.6	2.526	7.9	3.067	22	4.091
1.4	1.336	4.7	2.548	8	3.079	23	4.135
1.5	1.405	4.8	2.569	8.1	3.092	24	4.178
1.6	1.470	4.9	2.589	8.2	3.104	25	4.219
1.7	1.531	5	2.609	8.3	3.116	26	4.258
1.8	1.588	5.1	2.629	8.4	3.128	27	4.296
1.9	1.642	5.2	2.649	8.5	3.140	28	4.332
2	1.693	5.3	2.668	8.6	3.151	29	4.367
2.1	1.742	5.4	2.686	8.7	3.163	30	4.401
2.2	1.788	5.5	2.705	8.8	3.185	31	4.434
2.3	1.833	5.6	2.723	8.9	3.186	32	4.466
2.4	1.875	5.7	2.740	9	3.197	33	4.497
2.5	1.916	5.8	2.758	9.1	3.208	34	4.526
2.6	1.955	5.9	2.775	9.2	3.219	35	4.555
2.7	1.993	6	2.792	9.3	3.230	36	4.584
2.8	2.030	6.1	2.808	9.4	3.241	37	4.611
2.9	2.065	6.2	2.825	9.5	3.251	38	4.638
3	2.099	6.3	2.841	9.6	3.261	39	4.664
3.1	2.131	6.4	2.856	9.7	3.272	40	4.689
3.2	2.163	6.5	2.872	9.8	3.283	45	4.807
3.3	2.196	6.6	2.887	9.9	3.292	50	4.912
3.4	2.224	6.7	2.902	10	3.303	55	5.007
3.5	2.253	6.8	2.917	11	3.396	60	5.094
3.6	2.281	6.9	2.931	12	3.485	65	5.174
3.7	2.308	7	2.946	13	3.565	70	5.248
3.8	2.330	7.1	2.960	14	3.639	75	5.317
3.9	2.361	7.2	2.974	15	3.708	80	5.382
4	2.386	7.3	2.988	16	3.773	85	5.443
4.1	2.411	7.4	3.001	17	3.833	90	5.500
4.2	2.435	7.5	3.015	18	3.890	95	5.554
4.3	2.459	7.6	3.028	19	3.944	100	5.605

TABLE IV.

COMMON FRACTIONS WITH THEIR DECIMAL EQUIVALENTS.

Common fraction.	Decimal equivalent.	Common fraction.	Decimal equivalent.	Common fraction.	Decimal equivalent.
$\frac{1}{64}$	.0156 +	$\frac{11}{32}$	.3437 +	$\frac{43}{64}$	.6718 +
$\frac{1}{32}$	.0312 +	$\frac{23}{64}$	.3593 +	$\frac{11}{16}$	.6875
$\frac{3}{64}$	.0468 +	$\frac{3}{8}$	.375	$\frac{45}{64}$	.7031 +
$\frac{1}{16}$	.0625	$\frac{25}{64}$	.3906 +	$\frac{23}{32}$	.7187 +
$\frac{5}{64}$	.0781 +	$\frac{13}{32}$	.4062	$\frac{47}{64}$	.7343 +
$\frac{3}{32}$	.0937 +	$\frac{27}{64}$	.4218 +	$\frac{3}{4}$	.75
$\frac{7}{64}$	.1093 +	$\frac{7}{16}$	.4375	$\frac{49}{64}$	.7656 +
$\frac{1}{8}$	.125	$\frac{29}{64}$	.4531 +	$\frac{25}{32}$	.7812 +
$\frac{9}{64}$	.1406 +	$\frac{15}{32}$	.4687 +	$\frac{51}{64}$	.7968 +
$\frac{5}{32}$	.1562 +	$\frac{31}{64}$	.4843 +	$\frac{13}{16}$	.8125
$\frac{11}{64}$	.1718 +	$\frac{1}{2}$	.5	$\frac{53}{64}$	.8281 +
$\frac{3}{16}$	.1875	$\frac{33}{64}$	.5156 +	$\frac{27}{32}$	.8437 +
$\frac{13}{64}$	.2031 +	$\frac{17}{32}$	.5312 +	$\frac{55}{64}$	.8593 +
$\frac{17}{32}$	.2187 +	$\frac{35}{64}$	.5468 +	$\frac{7}{8}$	.875
$\frac{15}{64}$	.2343 +	$\frac{9}{16}$	.5625	$\frac{57}{64}$	.8906 +
$\frac{1}{4}$	.25	$\frac{37}{64}$	.5781 +	$\frac{29}{32}$	.9062 +
$\frac{17}{64}$	.2656 +	$\frac{19}{32}$	.5937 +	$\frac{59}{64}$	.9218 +
$\frac{9}{32}$	.2812 +	$\frac{39}{64}$	.6093 +	$\frac{15}{16}$	.9375
$\frac{19}{64}$	.2968 +	$\frac{5}{8}$	.625	$\frac{61}{64}$	.9531 +
$\frac{5}{16}$	.3125	$\frac{41}{64}$	.6406 +	$\frac{31}{32}$	.9687 +
$\frac{21}{64}$	.3281 +	$\frac{21}{32}$	.6562 +	$\frac{63}{64}$	.9843 +

CHAPTER XIX.

TESTING ENGINES AND BOILERS.

ABSOLUTE EXACTNESS NOT POSSIBLE.

EXPERT tests of engines and boilers, however care-fully and skilfully conducted, cannot be relied upon as being absolutely exact. There are chances for slight mistakes and elements of doubt which, while they may not very materially affect the results, will in a slight degree render them uncertain. The best that can be said of any tests of engines and boilers is that they are fairly accurate if the necessary care is taken in making them. But to be of any value every possible precaution should be taken to avoid and modify errors.

DIFFERENT WAYS OF MAKING TESTS.

There are several ways of testing a steam-engine. One of these—in which the heat in the exhaust-steam, that converted into work, radiated, etc., is accounted for—is too complicated for ordinary purposes, and will not be further referred to.

In one of the plans in common use account is taken of the coal burned, the result appearing as coal per horse-power per hour. By this plan the engine and boiler are considered together; hence it is a test of the steam-plant rather than of the engine. In some in-stances this may be exactly what is required; in others it is desirable to determine the economical efficiency of the engine without reference to the boiler furnishing the steam. Then it is customary to measure the water used, the result appearing as water per horse-power per hour. There is, generally speaking, less chance for error in calculating the economy of the plant as a whole than in finding that of either the engine or boiler separately.

DETERMINING THE COAL USED PER HORSE-POWER PER HOUR.

When this is what is required the work done by the engine in a given time is measured, and the coal burned in doing it weighed. A run of not less than 10 hours should be made when at all practicable; in fact it is better to extend the run to 20 or 24 hours. The greatest chances for error are at the beginning and conclusion of the test, and the greater the interval the less the final result will be affected by errors occurring at these times.

MEASURING THE INDICATED HORSE-POWER.

For this purpose diagrams from both ends of the cylinder at intervals of 15 minutes will ordinarily be sufficient. At the conclusion of the run these are to be calculated, and the average mean effective pressure of all used in determining the horse-power. This in most cases will give the mean horse-power practically correct; there may be special cases, when the power is extremely variable, where diagrams should be taken oftener than at intervals of 15 minutes. The judgment of the engineer must be used to get at a fair

average of the work done; nothing in the way of sug-
gestion can take the place of this.

Since measuring a large number of diagrams is somewhat tedious, it is always advisable to take precautions
to shorten this operation. If a planimeter is used for
measuring the area of diagrams it is worth while to be
at some pains to adjust the drum-motion to get them
even inches, or inches and half-inch, long. The process of computing the mean effective pressure by the
use of the planimeter consists in finding the mean
height of the diagram by dividing the area (taken from
the reading) by the length, then multiplying this height
by the scale of the spring. Sometimes the fractional
part of the length is very awkward, and makes the
process a long one. By a little attention the length of
the diagram may be made such that the division
will be much simplified, or that by cancellation with
the number representing the scale of the spring no
division will be necessary.

DETERMINING THE COAL BURNED.

This is by no means easy of accomplishment. Several plans, with various modifications, are employed,
each of which has its advocates. One is to raise steam
to working pressure, then draw the fire, and build a
new one, weighing and charging up all wood and coal
used to the termination of the test. To reduce the
wood to its equivalent in coal, multiply the pounds of
wood used by 0.4. Thus, if 50 pounds of wood are
used in starting the new fire the equivalent in coal will
be $50 \times 0.4 = 20$ pounds.

At starting the fire, the water-level and steam-pressure should be accurately noted, and these should be exactly the same at stopping the engine; they should also, as far as practicable, be kept constant during the entire run. The time of starting and stopping the engine should be carefully noted; the interval is the duration of the test.

Immediately at the conclusion of the test the fire should be drawn and quenched, and the unconsumed coal picked out, weighed, and deducted from that charged up as being used. If it is desired to find the combustible used, everything that comes from the fire during and at the conclusion of the test should be weighed and deducted.

The coal (and the equivalent in coal for the wood) supplied to the furnace, including that used in starting the fire, less the unconsumed coal weighed back, is the amount to be charged to the test. This divided by the average horse-power, and again by the duration in hours of the test, is the coal burned per horse-power per hour.

Suppose for a run of 10 hours the average horse-power is 200 and the coal burned 4000 pounds; 4000 divided by 200, and that again by 10, gives 2 pounds of coal per indicated horse-power per hour.

An objection to this test is that there will inevitably be some loss in hauling the fire and rebuilding, by cold air coming in contact with the heating surfaces and the brick-work. There is also likelihood of a small loss in picking out the unconsumed fuel.

After building a new fire it must get going sufficiently to keep up steam before the engine is started; for this reason I have always found it advisable that the steam be a little lower than the ordinary running pressure when the new fire is started. If the running pressure is 80 pounds, let it be 70 pounds when the fire is started, then start the engine when the pressure gets to 80 pounds; by this time the. fire should be in condition to keep up steam. The stop should be made at the conclusion of the test with the pressure at 70 pounds.

ANOTHER PLAN OF DETERMINING THE COAL BURNED.

Another plan is, before beginning the test, to clean the fire, and in the operation of cleaning — shoving back and distributing over the grate again—to estimate very carefully the quantity of clean coal on the grate, or at least to make such observations as will enable a comparison to be made with the fire similarly cleaned and treated at the conclusion. In this way the test can be begun and concluded without stopping the engine, unless it is necessary to do so to find the water-level, as in the instance of a boiler that raises the water considerably.

There is the objection to this test, that some error is certain in estimating the coal on the grate. If the fire is low when cleaned, and the test is of not less than 10 hours' duration, the error should not be serious. Of course all conditions should be the same, as near as may be, at starting and stopping; this is a requisite in any test of engine or boiler. Dependence should never be placed upon calculations by figures to equalize conditions, as, for instance, between observations at the beginning and termination of a test, when it is possible to make these conditions practically uniform.

WATER PER HORSE-POWER.

In the water-test of a steam-engine the water supplied to the boiler during the test is·weighed, and the total amount used divided by the average horse-power developed and by the duration, in hours, of the test. The result is water per indicated horse-power per hour. Thus, if, as before, the horse-power is 200, the duration of the test 10 hours, and the water used 40,000 pounds, then 40,000 divided by 200 and by 10 gives 20 pounds of water per horse-power.

A test of this kind can be begun at any time by noting the steam-pressure and water-level, and thereafter weighing the water supplied to the boiler. Some sort of tanks will have to be provided ; generally two barrels will answer. The arrangement should be such as to feed from one while the other is being filled.

The chief objection to a water-test is the possibility of considerable water being carried from the boiler to the engine with the steam. This water will be charged to the engine, when its presence is harmful rather than helpful. Plans for determining the amount of water present in the steam are in use, but so far there is no dependence to be placed upon them, as shown by the most contradictory results obtained. Until those who have given much attention and thought to testing the quality of steam are able to do satisfactory work it will be useless for others to attempt it, unless indeed they can devise a plan superior to any at present practised. With well-constructed boilers the water carried over with the steam is not a serious quantity. With overworked boilers of bad construction it may be a considerable percentage—say, 10 per cent—of all the water supplied.

PUMPING-ENGINE DUTY AND TESTS.

The economy of a pumping-engine is expressed by the use of the word "duty." This is the number of foot-pounds of work done by the consumption of 100 pounds of coal. Thus the duty of a pumping-engine that will do the equivalent of lifting 100,000,000 pounds one foot high for every 100 pounds of coal consumed is said to be 100,000,000. This has no reference to the capacity of the engine: that may be large or small. So far as the engine is concerned, this takes account of the effective and not the indicated power. It is usually calculated from the pressure against which the pump-piston works plus the equivalent pressure of lifting the water from the well. The resistance which the pump-piston must overcome is commonly determined by a pressure-gauge on the rising main : to the pressure indicated by this gauge is added the pressure due to its height above the water in the well, measured when the pump is working. This is found by multiplying the height in feet by 0.433, the result appearing in pounds pressure per square inch. The sum of these pressures will be the resistance against which the pump-piston works.

If this resistance is multiplied by the area of the piston in inches, the length in feet of a double stroke (revolution), the number of double strokes (revolutions) in a given time and by 100, and divided by the pounds of coal burned during that time, the quotient will be duty.

For example, let the area of pump-piston be 100 inches, double stroke four feet, number of double strokes 9600, coal burned 800 pounds, the gauge on main show a pressure of 50 pounds, and the height of this gauge above water in well be 23.1 feet. 23.1 × 0.433 = 10, which, added to 50 = 60 pounds, the resistance to motion of pump-piston. The duty will then be

$$\frac{60 \times 100 \times 4 \times 9600 \times 100}{800} = 28,800,000.$$

It will be understood that the last multiplier, 100, is used because the divisor is the number of pounds of coal burned instead of the number of hundred pounds.

Tests of pumping-engines may be begun either by starting new fires or estimating the amount of coal on the grate at the beginning and termination of the test. The water-pressure may vary considerably during the test, as when pumping direct into city mains, or since the dynamic head is the static head plus the friction when pumping into reservoirs, it will then vary with the speed of the pump; hence it is necessary to take the reading of the water-gauge at frequent intervals, say, each quarter hour, and average all the readings.

It is evident that the resistance against which the pump-piston moves might be calculated directly from diagrams from the pump-cylinder; but this is not customary. The indicator should be applied to the pump-cylinder and diagrams taken during the test to determine if the pump is working properly. If this is not done, it is possible to account for more work than is actually accomplished. Diagrams should also be taken from the steam-cylinder, and comparisons made with the power developed there and the work credited to the pump. I have known instances in which the pump was given credit for more work than was done in the steam-cylinder. Of course the reverse of this should be true to the extent of the friction of the engine.

Water-gauges, from the constant hammering they receive from the water, are subject to derangement, and sometimes, when the exact height to which the water is elevated is known, are not depended upon. In one test in which the writer was engaged the following plan for determining the dynamic head was pursued: The total height to which the water was raised was known to be 231.283 feet. This had been determined both by surveys and by testing the static head by a proved gauge. To determine how much to add for friction, the readings of the gauge were taken with engine at work and at rest, and the difference found to be 9.607 feet — one foot was added for friction below gauge. These added to 231.283 gave the dynamic head as 241.89 feet—in pounds, $241.89 \times 0.433 = 104.738$. It was believed that, although the gauge was not quite correct in total readings, it would not vary materially in less than 10 feet, equal to about 4 pounds. This view was further strengthened by the fact that the friction allowance agreed with previous estimates of the hydraulic engineers, so 104.738 pounds per square inch was taken as the resistance against which the pump-piston worked.

The custom has usually been in testing a pumping-engine to consider the plant—engine and boilers—as a whole. In fact from the understanding of the word duty it must be so considered. Sometimes, however, the duty guaranteed is on the assumption that the boilers will evaporate a specified amount of water per pound of coal; if they fail to do this, an allowance covering the deficiency is made in favor of the engine. This is generally to cover the possible use of a poor quality of fuel.

BOILER-TESTS.

In boiler-tests the object is to find the quantity of water evaporated per pound of coal, and the quantity the boiler is capable of evaporating. By one of the methods previously explained the coal burned in a given time is determined, and also the water evaporated. The latter is a measure of the capacity of the boiler, and divided by the former shows the economy. The difficulties previously mentioned—water carried over with the steam, and in accurately determining the coal burned—will of course be encountered.

In the preceding chapter the fact was alluded to that for uniformity it was customary to state the economy of a boiler in equivalent evaporation from and at 212°, and the process of making the reduction was explained. By the use of the following table, prepared for the *American Machinist* by a correspondent whose name I regret not being able to give, the process is very much shortened. The basis for this table are the steam-tables of Charles T. Porter. To use the table, multiply the observed evaporation by the factor under the pressure at which it took place, and against the temperature of feed. Thus, suppose the evaporation is 8½ pounds of water per pound of coal, the gauge-pressure being 80 pounds, and the temperature of feed 130°. Under 80 and against 130 find the factor 1.121. Multiply 8½ by this, and the product, 9.52, is the equivalent evaporation from and at 212°.

12

Table for Reducing to Standard the Observed Evaporation of a Boiler.

TEMPERA-TURE OF FEED.	GAUGE-PRESSURE, POUNDS PER SQUARE INCH.												
	30	40	50	60	70	80	90	100	110	120	130	140	150
32°	1.207	1.211	1.214	1.217	1.220	1.223	1.225	1.227	1.229	1.231	1.233	1.234	1.236
40°	1.199	1.203	1.206	1.209	1.212	1.214	1.217	1.219	1.221	1.223	1.24	1.226	1.228
50°	1.188	1.192	1.196	1.199	1.201	1.204	1.206	1.208	1.210	1.212	1.214	1.216	1.217
60°	1.178	1.182	1.185	1.188	1.191	1.194	1.196	1.198	1.200	1.202	1.204	1.205	1.207
70°	1.167	1.171	1.175	1.178	1.181	1.183	1.185	1.188	1.190	1.191	1.193	1.195	1.196
80°	1.157	1.161	1.165	1.168	1.170	1.173	1.175	1.177	1.179	1.181	1.183	1.185	1.186
90°	1.147	1.151	1.154	1.157	1.160	1.162	1.165	1.167	1.169	1.171	1.172	1.174	1.176
100°	1.136	1.140	1.144	1.147	1.150	1.152	1.154	1.156	1.158	1.160	1.162	1.164	1.165
110°	1.126	1.130	1.133	1.136	1.139	1.142	1.144	1.146	1.148	1.150	1.152	1.153	1.155
120°	1.116	1.120	1.123	1.126	1.129	1.131	1.134	1.136	1.138	1.140	1.141	1.143	1.145
130°	1.105	1.109	1.113	1.116	1.118	1.121	1.123	1.125	1.127	1.129	1.131	1.133	1.134
140°	1.095	1.099	1.102	1.105	1.108	1.110	1.113	1.115	1.117	1.119	1.120	1.122	1.124
150°	1.085	1.088	1.092	1.095	1.098	1.100	1.102	1.104	1.106	1.108	1.110	1.112	1.113
160°	1.074	1.078	1.081	1.084	1.087	1.090	1.092	1.094	1.096	1.098	1.100	1.101	1.103
170°	1.064	1.067	1.071	1.074	1.077	1.079	1.081	1.084	1.086	1.087	1.089	1.091	1.092
180°	1.053	1.057	1.060	1.064	1.066	1.069	1.071	1.073	1.075	1.077	1.079	1.080	1.082
190°	1.043	1.047	1.050	1.053	1.056	1.058	1.061	1.063	1.065	1.067	1.068	1.070	1.072
200°	1.032	1.036	1.040	1.043	1.045	1.048	1.050	1.052	1.054	1.056	1.058	1.059	1.061
210°	1.022	1.026	1.029	1.032	1.035	1.037	1.040	1.042	1.044	1.046	1.047	1.049	1.051

WHAT SHOULD BE NOTED.

As these tests are supposed to be made by working engineers and mechanics for purposes purely practical, the record will not usually be as complete as if made by experts for purposes partly scientific. In testing an engine it is necessary that the steam-pressure be accurately noted at intervals sufficiently short to insure a correct average. One of the objects of a steam-engine test is to determine the economy under a given steam-pressure; hence the importance of knowing exactly what that pressure is. If a condensing-engine, the vacuum by gauge should be similarly recorded, and other particulars given in Chapter V. When the boiler in any way enters into the test, temperatures in boiler-room and outside, and readings from a barometer when practicable, should be taken. If possible, the temperature of the escaping gases should be observed, and the temperature of the feed-water always; in fact, any conditions that remotely affect the result should, when possible, be recorded. Particularly dimensions and location of grate, dimensions of chimney, size, length, and number of tubes, and other parts, should be noted. Things that seem of no importance at the time may have value at some future consideration of the record. Measures and weights should be accurate, and gauges and other instruments known to be correct. The habit of being exact and of extending the observations made should be cultivated.

By practice and observation an engineer in charge of a steam-plant, or a machinist who sets up engines and boilers, may make tests that will assist in determining the most economical plan of operating, and with but little trouble or preparation. Such tests frequently made by engineers are valuable, and owners of steam-engines and boilers should in every way encourage them, as tending to greater economy in the use of fuel.

INDEX.

THE GAS ENGINE.

History and Practical Working.

BY DUGALD CLERK.

Illustrated by upward of 100 fine Engravings.
With Index.   12mo, cloth, $2.00.

CONTENTS:

HISTORICAL SKETCH OF THE GAS ENGINE,
1690 TO 1885.

PUBLISHED AND FOR SALE BY
JOHN WILEY & SONS, 53 E. 10th St., New York
₊ Mailed and prepaid on the receipt of the price.

SOME COMMENDATIONS.

"I have looked through the book with some care, and have laid it aside for careful study. I should say as the result of this first examination, that it is the most satisfactory treatise on the subject that I have yet seen."—Prof. R. H. THURSTON, *Sibley College, Cornell University.*

"From a hasty glance through (the book) I am convinced that it is a very thorough exposition of the subject, leaving nothing to be desired in regard to the theory of these Engines, and the results of practice, that is not found in this book."—Prof. W. P. TROWBRIDGE, *School of Mines, Columbia College.*

A TREATISE

UPON

Cable or Rope Traction

AS APPLIED TO THE WORKING OF

STREET AND OTHER RAILWAYS.

BY

J. BUCKNALL SMITH, C.E.

The chief object of this volume is to
describe the application and development of a comparatively novel system of
Mechanical Tractions for Street Railways,
known as the Endless Cable, Hanley's
System, as introduced in the United States,
New Zealand and Australia, and England.
Also a short treatise on the manufacture
of Wire and Wire Rope.

1 Vol., 4to, Cloth, Plates. Price, $2.50.

PUBLISHED BY

JOHN WILEY & SONS,

53 E. 10th St., New York.

WHOLLY PREVENTABLE AND CONTROLLABLE.

STEAM BOILER EXPLOSIONS,
IN THEORY AND PRACTICE.

By Prof. R. H. Thurston, Doc. Eng., Cornell University

12mo. Cloth, $1.50.

CONTENTS :

"This work ought to be in the hands of every steam-user. and if its directions are heeded, boiler explosions will become rare."—*Railroad Engineering Journal.*

"Prof. Thurston has given us, under the above caption, a work as useful as it is interesting."—*American Engineer.*

TWENTY YEARS WITH THE INDICATOR.

By THOS. PRAY, Jr.,

Consulting and Constructing Engineer, also C. and M.
E., Consulting Engineer of some of the largest
steam power users in the U. S.   Late editor
of *Boston Journal of Commerce and
Manufacturers' Gazette.*

1 vol.   8vo, cloth, $2.50.

This work is by a practical engineer of twenty-
four years' experience in adjusting all kinds of
engines, from the smallest portable to new and
largest locomotives and ocean steamships up to
1885.

Diagrams only from actual practice are given,
and all reproduced full size, with comments,
criticisms, reason why, how to do the best work,
and how to make all computations, both for practical and theoretical results, as well as compara-
tive.   The only method of the erection of theoretical and actual curve of expansion, original by
the author, and pronounced by scientific men as
absolutely correct.   Very profusely illustrated,
and with tables of value only ; the whole work is
in simple language, not a mathematical formulæ
in either book that any working engineer cannot
readily understand.

STEAM-ENGINES.

Stationary—Marine—Locomotive.

GAS-ENGINES.

STEAM-ENGINE CATECHISM. A series of thoroughly practical questions and answers arranged so as to give to a young engineer just the information required to fit him for properly running an engine. By Robert Grimshaw, M.E. 18mo, cloth. Eighth and enlarged edition $1 00

STEAM-ENGINE CATECHISM. Part II. Containing answers to further practical questions received since the issue of the first volume. By Robert Grimshaw, M.E. 18mo, cloth............. $1 00

THEORY OF THE STEAM-ENGINE. Translated from the fourth edition of Weisbach's Mechanics. By Prof. A. J. Du Bois. Containing notes giving practical examples of Stationary, Marine, and Locomotive Engines, showing American practice. By R. H. Buel. Numerous illustrations. 8vo, cloth..$5 00

STATIONARY STEAM-ENGINES. Especially adapted to Electric Lighting Purposes. Treating of the Development of Steam-Engines, the principles of Construction and Economy, with description of Moderate Speed and High-Speed Engines. By Prof. R. H. Thurston. 12mo, cloth................$1 50

TABLES, WITH EXPLANATIONS, RELATING TO THE NON-CONDENSING STATIONARY STEAM-ENGINE, AND OF HIGH-PRESSURE STEAM-BOILERS. By W. P. Trowbridge. Plates. 4to, paper boards $2 50

INDICATOR PRACTICE AND STEAM-ENGINE ECONOMY. With Plain Directions for Attaching the Indicator, Taking Diagrams, Computing the Horse-power, Drawing the Theoretical Curve, Calculating Steam Consumption, Determining Economy, Locating Derangement of Valves, and making all desired deductions; also, Tables required in making the necessary computations, and an Outline of Current Practice in Testing Steam-engines and Boilers. By Frank F. Hemenway, Associate Editor "American Machinist," Member American Society Mechanical Engineers, etc. 12mo, cloth...... .... $2 00

TWENTY YEARS WITH THE INDICATOR.
By Thos. Pray, Jr., C.E. and M.E. 1 vol. 8vo, cloth, $2 50
The work is by a practical engineer of more than nineteen
years' experience in readjusting and correcting, as well
as for power, economy, etc., of the steam-engine by the
indicator ; and no formula has been introduced except in
plain, simple language, concisely stated.

**MARINE ENGINES AND DREDGING-MA-
CHINERY.** Showing the latest and best English
and American Practice. By Wm. H. Maw. Illustrated by over 150 fine steel plates (mostly two-page
illustrations) of the engines of the leading screw
steamships of England and other nations, and
numerous fine wood-engravings. Folio, half mo-
rocco.................................... ....$18 00

**REPORT OF A SERIES OF TRIALS OF
WARM-BLAST APPARATUS FOR TRANS-
FERRING A PART OF THE HEAT OF
ESCAPING FLUE-GASES TO THE FUR-
NACE.** By J. C. Hoadley. A complete record of
a carefully conducted series of trials, with many
tables, illustrations, etc. 1 vol., 8vo, cloth....... $1 50

**LOCOMOTIVE-ENGINE RUNNING AND
MANAGEMENT.** A practical Treatise on the
Locomotive Engines, showing their performance
in running different kinds of trains with economy
and dispatch. Also directions regarding the care,
management, and repairs of Locomotives and all
their connections. By Angus Sinclair, M.E. Illustrated by numerous engravings. 12mo, cloth....$2 00

**LOCOMOTIVE ENGINEERING AND THE
MECHANISM OF RAILWAYS.** A Treatise on
the Principles and Construction of the Locomotive
Engine, Railway Carriages. and Railway Plant, with
examples. Illustrated by sixty-four large engravings and two hundred and forty wood-cuts. By
Zerah Colburn. Complete, 20 parts, $7.50; or 2
vols., cloth, $10 00. Half morocco. $15 00

THE GAS-ENGINE. History and Practical Working. By Dugald Clerk. With 100 illustrations.
12mo, cloth... . ...$2 00

**THE PRINCIPLES OF THERMO-DYNAM-
ICS.** With Special Applications to Hot-Air, Gas,
and Steam Engines. By Robert Röntgen. With ad-
ditions from Profs. Verdet. Zeuner, and Pernolet.
Translated, revised, and enlarged by Prof. A. Jay
Du Bois, of Sheffield Scientific School. 670 pages.
8vo, cloth.......................... ....$5 00